MW00426610

a
forgiveness
journal

LETTING
GO
OF
THE
PAST

kristin e. robertson

A Forgiveness Journal
Letting Go Of The Past
By Kristin E. Robertson

Copyright ©2009
Brio Leadership Press. All rights reserved.
Published by Brio Leadership Press, Colleyville, Texas.

No part of this publication may be reproduced, stored in a retrieval system, or transmitted in any form
or by any means, electronic, mechanical, photocopying, recording, scanning, or otherwise, except as
permitted under Section 107 or 108 of the 1976 United States Copyright Act, without the prior written
permission of the Publisher. Requests to the Publisher for permission should be addressed to Brio
Leadership Press, Colleyville, TX.

Limit of Liability/Disclaimer of Warranty: While the publisher and author have used their best efforts
in preparing this book, they make no representations or warranties with respect to the accuracy
or completeness of the contents of this book and specifically disclaim any implied warranties of
merchantability or fitness for a particular purpose. No warranty may be created or extended by sales
representatives or written sales materials. The advice and strategies contained herein may not be suitable
for your situation. You should consult with a professional where appropriate. Neither the publisher nor
author shall be liable for any loss of profit or any other commercial damages, including but not limited
to special, incidental, consequential, or other damages.

Copyeditor: Christine Frank, Christine Frank & Associates
Cover and Interior design: Toolbox Creative, www.ToolboxCreative.com
Author's Photo by Anne E. Dyson

Library of Congress Cataloguing-in-Publications Data
Library of Congress Control Number: 2009901050
Author Kristin E. Robertson
A Forgiveness Journal: Letting Go Of The Past
ISBN: 978-0-9823414-0-7
Library of Congress subject headings:
1. Self-help 2. Spirituality

2009

TABLE OF CONTENTS

INTRODUCTION

FORGIVENESS IS A SPIRITUAL VIRTUE found in all religious traditions. The Christ, when the disciple Peter asked him how often to forgive, taught us to forgive, not seven times, but seventy times seven. The Buddha said, "To understand everything is to forgive everything." In the Koran you find, "But forgive and overlook, till Allah brings his command."

The reason that all religions recommend forgiveness is that it is a process that can alleviate mental anguish and pain. Forgiveness can help you find the emotional equanimity that comes from being in touch with the Divine. Until you forgive yourself and your neighbors, you cannot sit in right relationship and integrity with yourself, with your neighbors, or with God. Forgiveness is a deeply spiritual journey to begin, one that is not without challenges.

Once you learn to forgive, your relationship with other human beings—in the family, the workplace, and with friends and acquaintances—will improve. You will begin to attract more like-minded people who will reinforce your loving attitudes. You will find harmony in many more relationships.

Forgiveness is like letting yourself out of prison. It is the key that you snatch from the jailer's keychain to get out from behind bars. If you are spending any mental or emotional energy on grievances, hurts, or negative incidents in your past that you can't let go of, you will benefit from the process of forgiveness. You do it for yourself, not for the person who hurt you.

You do not need to live a monk's life to practice forgiveness. Even if you can forgive just a little bit at a time, you can gradually set yourself free of your grievances and spiritually travel with a lighter load.

MY STORY

Like everyone, I have experienced my share of forgiveness opportunities, ranging from betrayals by friends and co-workers, an unintentional and thankfully short-lived abandonment by my mother, abandonment by a business partner, and being unfairly shut out of a substantial sum of money in a stock deal. I did not handle many of these grievances in the most spiritually mature way. I am embarrassed to admit that, in one instance, I cursed the person who hurt me by lighting black candles in her honor. In another case, I made myself sick by holding a grudge against a co-worker and not being able to forgive and accept what I perceived as a difficult situation at work. I developed both shingles (a stress-related disease) and walking pneumonia, which forced me to resign from my job. I knew at the time that I was hurting myself by not being able to forgive and accept what was reality, but I didn't have the spiritual tools or maturity to fix myself from the inside.

In more recent history, I began to realize how deeply I was wounding myself by not letting go of grievances and hurts. I knew that not accepting reality and not forgiving those who I perceived as my enemies were hurting only me—not the other person! How many times do you have to make yourself sick before you will change your ways? I wasn't willing to further jeopardize my health. I went about searching for a path to forgiveness.

And, as often happens, the universe provided me with an opportunity to develop a forgiveness process in real time. I experienced a large grievance story: A business partner in an altruistic endeavor "abandoned" (I use quotations because, with the passage of time, I now realize that it was a merciful separation) me in the midst of a difficult situation. I felt deeply angry and hurt, and walked around with a "how could you do this to me?" mentality for several months. Unhappy and miserable on the inside, I started experimenting with all the approaches to forgiveness that I knew about, reading books, listening to CDs, and praying and meditating until my knees were sore. During this journey, the fog of unforgiveness gradually lifted and I discovered that I had developed a process that might help others. During a long airplane flight, I documented the process with the help of the Divine, writing furiously in my journal to catch what I was hearing. I created a four-hour seminar and presented it at my church and other venues, and the idea for this book was born.

I share these less-than-honorable confessions with you to demonstrate the following points:

- Forgiveness is not an easy path to choose.

- You develop the ability to forgive at your own pace.

- Forgiveness is a process.

- The cost of not forgiving is compromised health, unhappiness, and an attachment to the past.

- The path to happiness is forgiveness.

As you develop your capacity to forgive, it becomes easier to forgive. The process takes less and less time. In fact, as you develop the capacity to forgive, you can prevent the need for forgiveness altogether by learning not to create a grievance story in the first place.

My goal in writing this is to come to a place in my journey where I am forgiving people in real-time, before I mentally construct a huge castle of interpretations around the incident, not after the fact. And my goal is to share with you what I have learned, in hopes that it will hasten your journey to real-time forgiveness.

HOW TO USE THIS JOURNAL

This booklet is meant to be used, not just read. The first section describes and walks you through a forgiveness process. You can read this section in one sitting if you wish, but the greatest benefit is derived if you do the exercises and write in this journal.

Because you will have multiple opportunities in your life to practice forgiveness, this booklet offers you six additional opportunities (seven opportunities in all) to walk through the steps in the process. The number seven was consciously chosen because of Christ's mandate to forgive seventy times seven, and to represent the seven days of the week and the chakras, the seven energy centers in the body. The additional pages do not include the narrative found in Section One. If you need more pages, you can purchase another *Forgiveness Journal* or use your own everyday journal to follow the steps.

The exercises in this journal are useful for multiple circumstances in life. You might find that after working through the entire process for one forgiveness opportunity, the next time you only need to pick and choose certain exercises to arrive at a sense of peace. Or you might find that a certain exercise is helpful to you when you are feeling fearful, or feeling a sense of scarcity instead of abundance. This book can be your toolbox for many challenges you face.

To get started, identify a grievance story that you'd like to work through.

WHY A JOURNAL?

This journal is a means to an end. Journaling is a proven and effective way to process your deepest thoughts and feelings by writing about them. Writing about feelings converts what are often pre-verbal concepts to concrete thoughts by moving the memories from the emotional brain to the analytical brain. Emotions are processed by a relatively primitive part of the brain called the limbic system, which also stores emotional memories. Language and writing are processed in the neo-cortex, an area of the brain capable of executive, or analytical, reasoning. Journaling dredges up your emotional memories from a primitive part of the brain and moves them to the analytical brain where you can think clearly and gain perspective.

Journaling also improves your health. Even though writing about your deepest thoughts and feelings may make you feel worse in the short term, your long-term health will improve. People who write about traumatic experiences are healthier than those who do not write about them.[1] The journalers make fewer visits to the doctor or health clinic than the other group.

Both my husband and I find journaling advantageous. We write probably three or four times a week, if not more often. Journaling is an effective way to work on your forgiveness skills. You will find that this journal, if used faithfully, provides a path to deeper peace, greater happiness, and the ability to travel through life with a lighter energetic load.

Do you want to be happy or to be right? Choose forgiveness and you will be happy.

● ● ●

---

[1] James W. Pennebaker, "Opening Up: The Healing Power of Expressing Emotions," The Guilford Press, August 8, 1997.

Part One:

How it
All
Starts

CHAPTER ONE
Building a Grievance Story

THE STATE OF NON-FORGIVING IS like drinking poison and expecting the other person to die. You hold on to grievance stories, which are the stories you create around a grievance incident, because you don't know any better. You haven't been taught to forgive, and you don't understand how the state of non-forgiveness hurts you and those you are intimate with. Let's start this examination by looking at the story of how Dan built a grievance story.

> Dan had been an executive for many years, reporting to the president of a small but growing firm. The president of the company, seeking to accelerate growth, decided to acquire another firm that had a complementary business. In doing so, the president re-organized the company so that Dan no longer reported to the president, but to a vice-president from the acquired company. In addition, the president moved some responsibilities from Dan's group to another team. Dan was angry at the president and fumed to his friends, "So this is the thanks I get for all my years of loyalty and hard work? He's cutting off my fingers knuckle by knuckle! How can I ever forgive him for humiliating me by reducing my job responsibilities?" Rather than seeing possibilities in the new company and his new position, Dan dug

in his heels, refusing to get along with his new boss and harboring anger
at the president for the injustices that Dan perceived. He immediately
started looking for another job and left the firm to take another, less
exciting job. Many years later, Dan wonders if he did the right thing.
Perhaps there was an alternative to getting angry and leaving—could he
have forgiven the president and worked out a way to stay in that exciting
company?

HOW DO YOU CREATE GRIEVANCE STORIES?

These are the steps that you typically take to create a grievance story in your mind:

1. The grievance or hurt: Someone does something to
    you. This grievance or hurt could be big or small. You
    might be passed over for a job promotion, your boss
    might give you a bad performance review, or your co-
    worker might steal your idea and claim it as his own.
    You might have been physically or psychologically
    abused. Or you may have been mistreated in some
    way. Someone may have given you a dirty look, rolled
    the eyes, or in some way disrespected you.

2. The interpretation: You interpret what happens to
    you through filters that have built up over lifetimes.
    Filters reflect seminal events and your interpretation
    of them, such as incidents from your childhood and
    adolescence, your ethnic and religious background,
    what your parents taught you both emotionally and
    ethically, and what might be going on in your present
    life. These elements form the basis for interpreting
    the event in your own special way. In the broadest
    sense, the event was neither good nor bad, but your
    interpretation may make it one or the other. You
    build up a story that assigns motives and importance
    to the actors in the drama. In your story, you are the

victim and the other is the villain, you are right and the other is wrong.

3. Suppression of emotions: Generally, people don't know how to work through their emotions in a healthy way after experiencing a grievance. If you have never been taught how to recognize and work through feelings, you tend to ignore them, to bottle them up, or build a wall around them. Instead of processing feelings in order to move through them, you get stuck in secondary emotions such as anger, feelings of revenge, hate, or self-loathing.

4. Story telling: You tell your family and friends about the grievance. They might reinforce your stance as a victim by sympathizing: "Oh, that's terrible. That was a horrible thing to do to you." The grievance catches hold of your mind and it builds in importance, gathering emotional strength the more you think and talk about it. You might find yourself telling complete strangers about this wound. The story-telling cements your interpretation of the event in your mind.

5. Endless instant replays: Every time you remember the grievance, you get angry or sad or depressed or vengeful all over again. Your mind plays endless re-runs of the hurt and negative emotions. You tend the fire of your emotional memories by continually stirring the ashes and adding wood, lest the fire be extinguished. Now you automatically get angry or upset at the slightest memory of the grievance. You are stuck in a rut of unhappiness, anger, and self-recrimination.

The amazing benefit of examining the process of developing a grievance story is that, once you understand it, you can stop the process and refrain from creating a grievance story in the first place. You can decide to be right or you can decide to be happy. If you choose to be right, you will get stuck in your grievance story, you will mentally portray the other person as a villain and you as a victim, and you will build up emotional energy around the event. If you choose to be happy, you will take steps to acknowledge and release your emotions about the incident (see steps one through three of A Forgiveness Process) but you won't cast yourself as a victim and the other as a villain. You won't tell your grievance story repeatedly and you will release it before it takes ahold of your brain.

For example, in the story above, Dan could have stepped back from his hurt and humiliation about the reorganization at work, decided to learn from it, and forged a strong working relationship with his new boss. He could have told himself that the president was only trying to make the company as successful as possible for everyone, rather than taking the new reporting structure as an affront and the president as the villain. He might have been able to stay at the company, learn new skills, and advance his career.

If you have grievance stories from the past, or can't help yourself from creating new ones (please be gentle on yourself—this is an evolutionary process), then you will find this booklet beneficial. The forgiveness process described in this booklet helps you break the cycle of continued upset by giving you the tools to work through your feelings, gain perspective, and realize that, in a mysterious and heavenly way, all is perfect. Only then can you begin to forgive.

THE BIG PICTURE

If you recognize that each person on this earth is a divine spirit in an earthly body, then there can be some acknowledgement that a divine hand is in everything that you experience. If you further acknowledge that everyone is connected energetically to each other and to a Higher Power (that some call God, Yahweh, Allah, Goddess, Beauty, or Truth), you can imagine that all souls are dancing together to some, as yet mysterious, heavenly music. Lastly, if you can acknowledge that everything happens for a reason and that your soul evolves most quickly when you learn to deal with earthly challenges such as suffering, then you can (almost) thank the other person who hurt you for presenting an opportunity to grow through the challenge of learning to forgive.

This is why forgiveness is a spiritual process. It is spiritual in the sense that it involves the human spirit, the essence of each person that yearns for wisdom, courage, and compassion. This essence is what makes you divine.

....

Building
a
Grievance
Story

CHAPTER TWO
The Nature of Forgiveness

Sally understands the nature of forgiveness. She made a decision years ago that she wasn't going to take anything personally anymore. Now, she consciously imagines the soul of the other person interacting with hers for a divine purpose. She is able to quickly let go of grievances and hurts by assuming benign intent on the part of the other person. She understands that when people do "bad" things, they are acting out of their own inner pain and misunderstanding. Although she has her moments of grief and despair, they are relatively short-lived. "Ever since I made the decision to not take offense at people, I'm much happier," says Sally. "I don't waste my energy on grudges, or gossip, or re-playing scenarios in my head. It's hard to explain, but life seems lighter, easier somehow."

WHAT IS FORGIVENESS?

Forgiveness is a decision and a process. Unless you are adept at it, it does not happen spontaneously. It takes some practice. The good news is that, with practice, you improve your ability to forgive and the speed with which you can do it.

Forgiveness is a way to let go of and accept the past so it doesn't hold any power over you. Once you release the past, your future is no longer limited by the painful memories of grievances or ingrained reactions. Forgiveness is the way *out* of playing the victim. It gives you the power to take charge of your life, to recognize that every player in the drama had a part to play, and to lovingly view each role with a heavenly perspective.

Forgiveness allows you to heal wounds from the past. It is a way of gaining perspective on what happened, allowing you to see situations from multiple viewpoints. Forgiveness should be targeted at both you yourself (self-forgiveness) and others.

Forgiveness is a profound inner journey that you choose to take.

MYTHS ABOUT FORGIVENESS

There is a great deal of misunderstanding about forgiveness—it is not what you may think. Forgiveness, as defined in this journal, is *not* about:

- Just forgetting about the incident. This approach denies you the opportunity to work through your reactions to the incident and develop some deeper understanding about yourself and human nature. Let's face it—forgetting is impossible unless you build a big, thick wall around the part of you that was hurt. Dividing yourself is not a path to wholeness; it is a path of denial. Remembering the incident while neutralizing the emotional charge is much more preferable than forgetting about it.

- Repressing your feelings about a situation. Instead, feel your emotions fully in order to move through and beyond them. If you "stuff" or repress your feelings about a situation, those emotions turn inward on you, causing short- and/or long-term health consequences and making you unhappy and depressed. Likewise, if you paint over the hurt with platitudes that minimize the pain, such as, "This too shall pass" or "It was only money," you deny yourself the chance to work through the hurtful feelings. Only by working through feelings can you get beyond them.

- Failing to take action to stop abuse or stand up for you. People who have committed criminal or unlawful acts should bear the natural consequences of their behavior. It is not your duty to protect them from reaping what they have sown. Forgiveness does not preclude allowing the natural or legal consequences of a poor decision on someone's part.

- Having to be friends with the person you forgive. Because this is inner work on yourself, you can reap the benefits of forgiveness without ever seeing or talking to the other person again. It's OK to decide that you don't like the other person and he or she is no longer welcome in your life.

BENEFITS OF FORGIVENESS

Forgiveness is beneficial to your mental and physical health. Typically, people who forgive are more optimistic, more hopeful, and more loving than others who don't learn to forgive.[2] They are also healthier, due to the effect that positive emotions have on your physical health. Human beings who tend toward happier emotions also tend to need to see the doctor less often and complain of fewer debilitating illnesses. Because forgiving people are more emotionally stable, they have fewer mental illnesses such as depression.

Forgiveness allows you to be happy. The pursuit of happiness is a basic human right, as least in the United States. More than just pursuing happiness, forgiveness can clear the way to *attaining* happiness. People who can gain perspective about negative life experiences and derive some value from these incidences are happier. Happiness is about accepting what you

2 Fred Luskin, "Forgive for Good," HarperOne, January 21, 2003.

have rather than wanting something you don't have. The more you forgive, the happier you will be.

Lastly, the saints and mystics in all religions extol the merits of emotional mastery and emotional equanimity. The great spiritual teachers recognize that humans without any techniques to manage the hundreds of emotions that we feel each day get stuck in their emotions. Emotional mastery is not the absence or ignoring of human emotions, but the allowing of them to arise in you, persist with your recognition for a time, and then to release them. Emotional mastery is needed for spiritual development, and forgiveness is one of the techniques, along with gratitude, that propels you along the path to emotional mastery.

Do these benefits sound like something you'd be interested in attaining? Read on for a process that will lead you to forgiveness and all its benefits.

Part Two

A
Forgiveness Process

IN THIS JOURNAL, YOU WILL be given the opportunity to work through seven grievances or hurts. Chapters Four through Ten will walk you through your first grievance with full detail and explanation of the exercises. Then, only the exercises will be repeated in the following journal pages.

Grievances come in different sizes—some are large, some are small, and some are in between. A large grievance might be an incident of physical violence such as a rape, abuse, or attack. It could be an incident involving a large sum of money, like when your uncle or friend convinced you to invest in a hot stock and you lost every penny of it. Or a large incident might be a major betrayal by a loved one, such as the infidelity of a spouse.

Grievances can be hurts, pains, or losses. The death of a loved one, whether it is a parent, a spouse, or a child, is a major trauma and can represent a forgiveness opportunity. You may be angry at God or the universe, or the situation, and you may be struggling to accept what happened. These are appropriate issues to work on in this book.

Many people cannot forgive a big grievance in one fell swoop. It may take you months or years to fully forgive and accept, but it is important to work at it. You may find that in experimenting with some of these exercises, you can gradually reduce the weight of the grievance on your spirit.

Although it is admirable to start with the biggest grievance you can think of, you will probably get the most benefit at first from starting on something smaller. You may have a list of grievances already prioritized in your mind. Choose the second on the list to get started with! Chances are that by working on the lesser one, you will be paving the way to work on the bigger one.

For example, you may want to forgive your mother for abandoning you when you were young. You recognize that this experience has influenced the way you react to many other things in life. You'd like to explore ways of forgiving your mother because it seems like that would make you happier. However, recently a close friend started ignoring your calls and, when confronted, announced that the friendship was over because it was no longer "comfortable." Notice that both of these incidents follow a pattern—they both involve people rejecting you in some way. By working on forgiving the friend, you will work with a recent incident that has had less time to get ingrained in your thinking, and thus have a higher probability of success. You will also, because of the similarity of the incidents, make yourself ready to tackle the larger issue with your mother.

So think of a relatively recent grievance story that is medium in size rather than tackling the biggest one first. Get some positive results from the first before attempting the bigger one.

Your forgiveness opportunity

Since you were attracted to this journal, you probably
already have one or more grievance stories that you'd like to
work on. Choose the second-most important story to explore
first. Briefly describe the situation here:

_____

_____

_____

_____

_____

_____

_____

● ● ●

CHAPTER THREE
Step One: Identify Your Feelings

Jay, a successful entrepreneur, grew up with an abusive father who followed the rule of "spare the rod, spoil the child." Jay's father often beat Jay with a belt whenever Jay talked back to him or disobeyed the rules of the house. His mother endured similarly rough treatment at the hands of Jay's father. The father would often hit or push his wife when provoked. Jay learned no language for expressing his feelings, especially anger, that seemed to overcome him when he was challenged by his peers. He was frequently in trouble at school for fighting with other boys.

Jay was ambitious, independent, and spunky. He left home at age 18 and never returned, working himself through college. He married a talented and lovely woman, with whom he had two boys of his own. Jay, acting in the only way that he knew how, began to use violence on his young boys when they disobeyed him." One night, after he had harshly spanked his youngest son, his wife packed up the two boys and left the house, screaming, "I can't live this way anymore! I won't have you taking out your anger on my poor innocent boy." After a long night of soul-searching, Jay realized that his marriage and family life was becoming a repeat of his own boyhood. It was at this point that Jay knew he needed to do something to heal his past. He found his wife at a friend's house and promised to get professional help if she would come home with the children.

Working with a counselor, Jay found that writing about the traumas he endured at the hands of his father allowed him to work through his pain and finally release the pent-up anger he carried towards his dad. "This process freed me up to be more loving with my own family," Jay remarks. "It's hard to explain, but now I am mentally clear enough to be aware of my angry reactions to the kids and stop the spankings and hitting. Before, it was like my anger at Dad colored everything I did."

Much has been written about emotional intelligence. Emotional intelligence (sometimes referred to as EQ) is your ability to recognize and manage your emotions and to manage your social relationships. EQ is a more reliable indicator of future success in life than intellectual prowess or IQ. You can prove this in your own experience by thinking back to your high school valedictorian, who was the brainiest person in the class, but probably is not the one who went on to become a U.S. senator, loving parent, successful entrepreneur, or high-ranking executive.

One of the basic skills in emotional intelligence is being able to identify your emotions. Sadly, only about a third of the population can accurately name emotions as they happen. Identifying feelings is a challenge for most people. Yet, without identifying and dealing with your emotions about a grievance story, you will not be able to move through them and heal them. Denial is not a viable coping method!

In this step, you can choose from two methods to identify emotions: writing about the grievance story and the body test. You will have the opportunity to explore the role of unmet human needs that contribute to how you feel about the situation.

WRITING ABOUT EMOTIONS

These are five categories of emotion words: those that express fear, anger, sadness, happiness, and love. Human beings feel positive emotions when their underlying needs are met, and negative emotions when their needs are not met. Why are there so many more "negative" than "positive" emotions? Negative emotions were more important to the species' survival in prehistory, causing the human being to develop the ability to detect fine gradients in negative emotions. For example, in the early history of humanity, a person's swift perception of fear could mean the difference between perishing and surviving when a fierce animal was about to attack. Conversely, gradients of love and happiness have not been as important to the survival of the species.

All emotions are derivatives of four basic rhyming words, making them easy to remember. The four basic emotions are:

- Bad

- Mad

- Sad

- Glad

You are on your way to emotional self-awareness when you can say, "I feel bad" (or mad, sad, glad) in the moment that you feel that emotion. However, as you gain expertise in naming emotions, you will naturally seek more exact expressions of your feelings. You will get to be adept at recognizing and knowing exactly what kind of "bad" or "glad" you feel, and you will notice the subtle differences between the emotions. The following list of emotion words gives you a good vocabulary to use in describing your feelings.

Identify
Your
Feelings

List of common emotion words

Fear	Bad Guilt Anxiety Unworthy Panic Petrified	Depressed Lethargy Apathy Embarrassed Disappointed Nervous
Mad	Anger Rage Disgust Resentful Bitter Irritated Frustrated	Annoyed Vengeful Impotent Defiance Blame Boredom
Sad	Hopeless Sorrow Depressed Drained Lonely Miserable	Upset Discouraged Helpless Ashamed Hurt Bad
Glad	Happy Content Pride Peace Elation Relief Anticipation	Equanimity Calm Enthusiastic Excited Cheerful Satisfied
Love	Joy Friendship Exultation Reverence Serenity Security	Gratitude Forgiveness Delighted Eager Open Hopeful

Identify
Your
Feelings

Tear out for your use.

From: A Forgiveness Journal by Kristin E. Robertson © 2009

You will use this list of emotions in the exercises that follow in this chapter. But first, consider one more element.

UNDER THE FEELING LIES A HUMAN NEED

In addition to identifying emotions, it is helpful to understand the human needs that underlie an emotion. When you experience a negative emotion, either bad or sad, it is because your needs are unmet. Likewise, when your needs are met, you are likely to experience a positive emotion. Looking at a combination of feelings and unmet needs provides a complete perspective on your grievance story.

The following is a list of common human needs, which are provided to help you identify what need went unmet for you in your grievance story.

List of common human needs[3]

Autonomy	• To choose one's dreams, goals, values • To choose one's plans for achieving one's dreams
Celebration	• To celebrate creations of life • To celebrate losses in life
Integrity	• Authenticity • Creativity • Meaning • Self-worth
Play	• Fun • Laughter
Spiritual Communion	• Beauty • Harmony • Inspiration • Order • Peace

continued...

3 Permission granted by (c) 2005 by Center for Nonviolent Communication
www.cnvc.org   cnvc@cnvc.org 818.957.9393

Physical Nurturance	▪ Air ▪ Food ▪ Movement/ exercise ▪ Rest/sleep	▪ Sexual expression ▪ Safety ▪ Shelter ▪ Touch ▪ Water
Meaning	▪ Awareness ▪ Celebration of life	
Inter-Dependence	▪ Acceptance ▪ Appreciation ▪ Closeness ▪ Community ▪ Consideration ▪ Contribution to the enrichment of life ▪ Emotional safety	▪ Empathy ▪ Honesty ▪ Love ▪ Reassurance ▪ Respect ▪ Support ▪ Trust ▪ Understanding ▪ Warmth

In the following exercises, please give yourself the gift of listening for your feelings and underlying needs. Make the goal of these exercises to truly understand yourself.

Exercise: Identify your feelings

In the following exercises, write about your grievance story. Writing about a traumatic experience can be healing. Writing brings the memories from the part of your brain that stores emotional memories into the analytical brain, also called the neocortex. This "airing" of your feelings allows you to use your higher mental processes in making sense of the situation.

When you think of your forgiveness opportunity, what are the primary emotions that you feel? Please refer to the list on page 33.

_____

_____

_____

_____

_____

_____

What were your unmet needs in the situation? Please refer to the list of human needs on page 35.

_____

_____

_____

Now, please write for about ten minutes about your deepest thoughts and emotions about your forgiveness opportunity. If you begin to feel a strong emotion, stay with it but try to observe it from an objective point of view. As you observe it in this manner, its intensity will fade.

Here are two contrasting examples of writing. The first is factual writing and the second is expressive writing.

Factual writing: "When my little sister was born, my mom arranged with my grandmother to pick up my younger brother and me and take us to her house. We were to stay there with her for several days, until my mom returned from the hospital. I did not know this plan. When Grandma arrived to fetch us, she put us in the back seat of the car and drove to her home, 45 minutes away. I stared out the back window the whole time. I don't remember what my brother did."

Expressive writing: "When my little sister was born, my mom arranged to have my grandmother, who I considered the Wicked Witch of the West, to bring my brother and I to live with her until my mom returned from the hospital. Mom had failed to tell me of her plans before my sister was born. When Grandma arrived, I started to cry and stomp my feet. I hated my grandmother! I was confused and heartbroken that my mommy was gone, and I didn't understand why

Mom wasn't there to take care of me. I didn't want
to go. My grandma threw my brother and I into the
back seat of her car and angrily drove off, muttering
something about little girls and their tantrums. I
felt totally abandoned, left in the hands of a mean-
spirited old woman for whom I felt no love. I cried
the whole way to Grandma's home, looking out the
back window and hoping that my mommy would come
and rescue me from this horrible woman. To this day,
the memory of that drive makes me feel small and
alone. And I'm sure it is a big reason why I have such
friction in my relationship with my sister."

The objective in this exercise is to notate your deepest
feelings and thoughts as expressively as possible. Do not hold
back on your emotions. The healing will come because of the
deep feelings that you describe and express. This is a safe place
and way of expressing yourself with full honesty. No one needs
to see these pages but you. Please write for at least ten minutes.
It is best to complete this exercise in one sitting, just letting the
words pour out of you.

_____

_____

_____

_____

_____

_____

_____

_____

_____

_____

_____

Please do not be discouraged if, at this point, you feel worse than you did before. This is typically a passing mood, brought on by the deep inner work that you have just completed. Advancing to the next step in this process may help lighten your mood.

If you are concerned, however, about the intensity of your feelings, or if you are feeling that you could be a threat to the safety of yourself or others, please call 911 or seek immediate mental health care in your community.

Exercise: The body test for feelings

The following exercise is an alternative method for identifying your feelings. You can use this exercise often during the day to help you become more attuned to the natural ebb and flow of emotions that we each experience.

All emotions are expressed, either subtly or strongly, in the body. You cannot have an emotion that doesn't register somewhere in your body. You can understand this through your own experience: When you are embarrassed, you involuntarily blush. When you are happy, you smile or laugh. When you are extremely sad, you cry. When you are nervous, you get butterflies in the stomach.

Although each body reacts in its own unique way, there are some areas of the body that tend to hold certain feelings. One way to get in touch with your emotions is to mentally scan your body to detect physical clues to what you are feeling. This test can be done quickly and discreetly, with your eyes open or closed, at any time of the day when you want to be aware of your emotional state. It is best done when you are sitting quietly.

For the purposes of identifying the feelings associated with your past hurt, bring to mind your grievance story. Mentally replay the incident as if you were experiencing it once more. It's best not to view this like a movie in which you are watching yourself—instead, imagine what it looked, felt, smelled, and sounded like from your own perspective and within your own skin. When you perceive that your feelings are at their height, begin the exercise.

To do the body test for feelings, soften the gaze of your eyes or close them gently. Direct your attention to your head first. Notice if you feel any tension there. If so, most likely you are feeling some fear or anxiety. Label the feeling by saying to yourself, "I feel afraid."

Next bring your attention to the neck and throat area. Do you feel any constriction or tingles there? If so, it might indicate sadness and you can acknowledge it by mentally saying, "I feel grief or sadness."

Now direct your focus to your mid- and upper-back and shoulders. If you feel tension or tightness there, it might indicate anger. Say, "I feel angry or mad."

Lastly, focus your attention on your navel and solar plexus area. Tightness here usually indicates fear, guilt, or nervousness. If so, say, "I feel guilty/nervous/afraid."

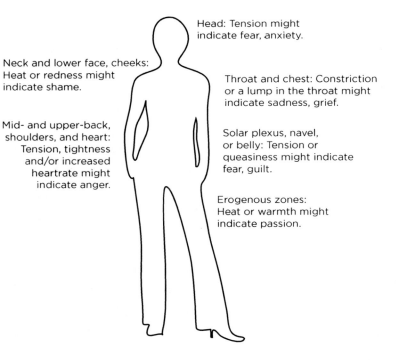

Head: Tension might indicate fear, anxiety.

Neck and lower face, cheeks: Heat or redness might indicate shame.

Mid- and upper-back, shoulders, and heart: Tension, tightness and/or increased heartrate might indicate anger.

Throat and chest: Constriction or a lump in the throat might indicate sadness, grief.

Solar plexus, navel, or belly: Tension or queasiness might indicate fear, guilt.

Erogenous zones: Heat or warmth might indicate passion.

Remember to love and appreciate yourself as you do this. Test quickly and often during the day, and you will become more familiar with the unique way your own body expresses and holds emotion.

CHAPTER FOUR
Step Two: Talk it Out

Once Jay wrote about his childhood and the pent-up feelings he had ignored for years, he found he needed the skill of a counselor to listen to his story and guide him through a forgiveness process. It was Jay's counselor that encouraged Jay to tell his story to his wife. Jay was fortunate that his wife, Ellen, could listen to him with patience and compassion, despite the hurt that he had caused her. Ellen said, "I was just glad that we were talking and that Jay finally opened up to me." Ellen was amazed at what she heard. "When Jay started telling me the stories of how he grew up, how violent his Dad was toward him and how he was always angry as a boy," says Ellen, "I began to have a deep appreciation for all that he overcame to become who he is today. Before this, I had only a small inkling of what went on in his childhood. Our marriage has become much stronger because he was able to confide his deepest feelings about the abuse he endured."

Now that you have identified your emotions using the body test and journaling, it is time to turn to another human being to help you process the incident and your interpretation of it.

Talk therapy is based on the same principle as this step. It is enormously helpful to have another human being deeply listen to you and your story. To connect with another, to be understood by another, is a basic human need. For some, this may be the first time you have told your story to another person.

Talking about the situation is often helpful, but you must choose your partner carefully. Your partner should:

- Listen without judging you

- Not contribute to your grievance story

- Empathize and acknowledge your feelings

- Help you see another perspective of the situation

Some people are not capable of providing the neutrality you need in this instance. Do not choose someone to talk to who will sympathize with you or make you more angry or vengeful than you were before. Specifically ask the chosen person to listen respectfully and acknowledge your feelings. Do not let the person express negative thoughts about the person who hurt you. The point of this exercise is not to throw a pity party, but to advance your healing through human-to-human connection.

You should consider engaging the services of a professional counselor, coach, or therapist if you feel that:

a. None of your friends or family members possess the neutrality needed for this step, or

b. You have some major issues to resolve.

The money you spend on a therapist will be well worth it. Paying someone to listen to and guide you is the best investment you can make in your own mental health. And the benefits of getting your mind and emotions unstuck from this grievance are limitless.

There are a number of ways to find a therapist who is a good fit for you: Ask your friends for a referral to a competent therapist in your area. Check your insurance company for listings of professionals who are in-network for you. Ask your primary care doctor, your clergy, or other care-related professionals you know for a referral.

How much talking is too much? There is a limit on talking about your grievance, past which you can get stuck in the rut of your repetitive, angry thoughts. Do not pave that rut in your brain! Native Americans have a tradition of allowing tribal members to tell their grievance story three times. After that, you are ignored because it is time to move on. This is a good rule for you to follow: Stop telling your grievance story after three times. I find that following this rule forces me to choose carefully and wisely the people that I share it with, so I get maximum benefit from the limited number of times I repeat the story. I want to explore my emotions fully, but I don't wish to gossip, make the other person the villain, or wallow in my wounds. From personal experience, I know not to deeply ingrain my victim mentality by repeating my story too many times.

Exercise: Talking it out

At some point, you may wish to share your forgiveness opportunity story with a friend, partner, or confidante.

With whom did you choose to share?

_____

Describe how your talk went and how you felt after it:

_____

_____

_____

_____

_____

CHAPTER FIVE
Step Three: Change Viewpoints

When Jay worked on this step, he realized that he didn't know much about his father, including what Dad experienced during his youth or during Jay's childhood. Both Jay's dad and mom were deceased, but he had a close relationship with his father's younger sister, Aunt Ida. He called her to ask questions about his father. What he discovered affected him profoundly. His aunt told him that his father had been a gentle, albeit conflicted, man until he went off to become a soldier. Jay's dad had been captured and held prisoner for several years, enduring unthinkable torture and abuse at the hands of the enemy. Ida said that she thought he had suffered some injury to his head during this time, and he was never the same after returning from the war. Jay asked why no one had ever revealed this story to him, and Aunt Ida replied simply, "We didn't talk about unpleasant things in our family."

Jay was lucky—he discovered the most likely cause of his father's abusive behavior. You may not be able to identify the cause of the other person's behavior, but you can guess. Try to put yourself in the shoes of the other person and imagine what they might have been feeling at the time of your grievance story. What might have been going on in his life? What in their background may have caused her to act as she did? If you can imagine this, you can make an estimate of their emotions and unmet needs.

In order to let go, it is important to consider the other person's or party's point of view. This keeps you from perpetuating your grievance story and helps you get out of the rut of negative thinking that a brain can get stuck in. I'm sure you're familiar with that rut—every time something reminds you of the grievance, your mind races down the road of self-pity, anger, revenge, and victim thinking. If you are paving that rut in your brain, it is time to change viewpoints. Don't worry—you can re-pave your brain to go down different, more productive pathways in the future.

This may be an intellectual exercise for now. Be gentle with yourself: If this is hard, give yourself ample time to complete the exercises. You may need to set aside the process for now and return to it in a day or two.

Exercise: Change viewpoints

Think about your grievance story and what you knew about the other person. What might have been going on in his life that made him act the way he did? For example, if your grievance story involves a parent, write about what aspects of her upbringing or the difficulties she was grappling with at the time of your story.

Or, you can ask yourself, what would cause *me* to act this way? What could have happened to me to motivate me to do the same? What in my history, my beliefs, the way my parents raised me, the traumas, etc. might have caused me to be like the other person?

_____

_____

_____

_____

_____

_____

_____

_____

_____

_____

Were there some challenges or difficulties she was facing? What else might he have been dealing with that you weren't aware of? What emotions might the other person have felt? Please refer to the list of emotions on page 33. What were the other person's needs? Please refer to the list of human needs on page 35. Take time to write about what the other person might have been feeling and what his needs were:

_____

_____

....

_____

Change
Viewpoints

_____

_____

Exercise: Taking responsibility for your part

In this exercise, you are asked to identify your contribution to or role in the grievance story. You may think that this is not a fair request of a hurt person. For example, you may say that offenses such as child abuse should never be blamed on the child. I agree with that statement. Children are vulnerable, powerless beings in an abusive family environment. But in my experience, there is often some residual guilt that the abused feels while they process their memories as an adult. Guilt might be the result of errors of commission or omission, meaning that the abused might have cooperated with the perpetrator in some small way, or the abused may have refrained from telling an authority figure about the abuse. The abuser may have threatened the child to keep their relationship "our little secret," making the child afraid to tell anyone else about it. This causes deep anguish for the adult who was abused, wishing they had spoken up to a caring authority figure. The grown-up child needs to process this anguish.

If this step is too difficult for you, skip it for now and come back to it when you are ready.

What did you do to contribute to the situation? In every situation, there is something—some action that you took or didn't take—that you feel responsible for. This is an account-ability step, and it also identifies what you may need to forgive in yourself.

_____

_____

_____

_____

_____

_____

_____

I wish to forgive myself for the part I took in creating this grievance. Specifically, I wish to forgive myself for:

_____

_____

_____

_____

_____

_____

_____

CHAPTER SIX
Step Four: Gain Perspective

Betty had worked hard on trying to forgive her first husband, who had run up credit card debt without her knowing. After she finally divorced him, she started to receive notices about unpaid credit cards that were held jointly in her name. "I was so angry when I first received those dunning notices," Betty fumed. "I thought I had gotten rid of that loser by divorcing him, but Andy's credit history kept dogging me! Because I trusted him during our marriage, I had signed several credit card applications he made, and I had to pay thousands of dollars of his debt just to clear my name! How can I ever forgive him?" Betty knew that she had some hard inner work to do to let go of her bitterness towards Andy and forgive him. It wasn't until she was able to do some of the exercises in this section that she finally felt his grip on her spirit loosening. "When I did the heavenly perspective exercise, it all dropped into place for me. I started thinking about what I needed to learn in this situation and what God wanted me to do," she added."

You are at the mid-point of this seven-step process. This step is the pivotal transition step, just like Wednesday is the pivotal day in the work week ("hump day" in current parlance) when you can start looking forward to the weekend. Similar also is the heart or fourth chakra, which represents the transition from ego-based energy centers in the human body to spirit-based energy centers. At this mid-point, you have processed your own emotions and needs and considered those of the other person. You have done good interior work, digging deeply into your psyche to bring aspects of your story to light that had been tucked away in your memory. Now you turn to expanding your view of the situation. You turn your focus from the earthly to the more heavenly opportunities in your grievance story.

Perspective helps you get out of your grievance story and see the situation from another person's viewpoint. *A Course in Miracles* defines a miracle as a change in perspective. When you can see your grievance story from multiple new perspectives, you begin to see it from a more holistic or heavenly point of view. The miracle occurs when you are successful in releasing your own narrative of the grievance story and consider that there might be other narratives and ways to look at the situation.

The exercises in this section can help you re-frame any challenge you encounter, even if you don't consider it a grievance story. For example, you may feel anxious about the choices that your teenaged child is making, or the state of the economy or your job security. To gain perspective, you might work through some of the exercises in this section. You might find that answering these questions sparks your creativity and allows you to see solutions that might not have been obvious before.

This step is especially helpful to those who need to forgive themselves for past actions that they regret. In self-forgiveness, it is extremely important to seek a big-picture perspective. I sometimes try to perceive myself as if I were my own child. I mentally envision how I would talk to and comfort myself as a little child who had done something wrong. I also invoke the heavenly perspective to attempt to see the perfection in all.

There are some situations I experience in which I feel like an actor in someone else's play. Typically, those are the situations in which I've behaved out of character, or embarrassingly badly. In those situations, I sense there might be a hidden sacred contract between me and the person I treated poorly, a contract meant to allow one of us to learn some important spiritual lesson. I am not privy to the knowledge of what that lesson is because of its hidden, heavenly nature. Just acknowledging the possibility of a hidden sacred contract is often helpful in creating space for me to forgive myself.

Here are several tools to help you gain perspective.

Exercise: Newspaper reporter

Pretend you are a newspaper reporter and write a short article about your forgiveness opportunity. Use the third person, and include only the facts (who, what, when, where, how).

_____

_____

_____

_____

_____

Exercise: The wide-angle lens

What were the positive aspects or results of the situation? Did you learn something, develop skills? What gifts did you receive because of this? If sufficient time has not passed for this to become evident, imagine what benefits might come from this situation.

_____

_____

_____

_____

_____

Exercise: Deathbed memories

How will you remember this at the end of your life? Will
you even remember it?

_____

_____

_____

_____

_____

_____

Exercise: The heavenly perspective

The purpose of this exercise is to get you out of your
narrow perception, out of your skin, so to speak, and challenge
you to see the situation from God's point of view. The challenge is to see it in its perfection, to see it from the all-loving
eyes of the Divine, and to see that perhaps the whole situation
is not all that important in the heavenly scheme of creation.

Sit quietly in your chair and either close your eyes or
soft-focus them on a spot on the floor. Relax your body and
take a deep breath.

Imagine yourself in your grievance story, with all of its
problems, dark emotions, and difficulties. Picture a scene
that represents the issues you are grappling with and picture
yourself in that scene. What are you doing, feeling, and saying?
Once you get a clear picture of this scene, make a clone of your
spirit and assign it the job of "observer." Make your observer
spirit fly up to the rooftop to view this scene with your spirit's
X-ray vision. What do you observe from the rooftop?

_____

_____

_____

_____

Now send your spirit up to the clouds and have it view the scene with you in it. What does your spirit observe from the clouds?

_____

_____

_____

_____

Now send your spirit up to the moon and have it view the scene with you in it. What does your spirit observe from the moon?

_____

_____

_____

_____

Gain
Perspective

Now send your spirit up to heaven, where it can perceive all of the cosmos. Ask your spirit to view the scene back on earth. Then tell your spirit to consult with a Divine entity (you might call it God, Goddess, Allah, or others) to determine if there is a Divine meaning to what is going on in the scene on earth. Listen closely and note what your spirit tells you from heaven.

_____

_____

_____

_____

Come back to earth and slowly open your eyes. Breathe deeply.

Exercise: The hero perspective

In order to turn around a grievance story, you need to paint yourself as the hero in the story. Focus on the amazing resilience you showed—after all, you survived, didn't you? How were you the hero in this story?

_____

_____

_____

_____

_____

_____

_____

_____

_____

_____

_____

_____

_____

_____

_____

_____

_____

_____

● ● ●

CHAPTER SEVEN
Step Five: Letting Go

Betty described it this way: "I had gotten so used to thinking of Andy as the bad guy and me as the victim. I think my friends were tired of hearing me gripe about him—in fact, I may have lost a friend who couldn't put up with my whining about the situation. But others kept telling me that I was right and he was wrong. I know they were only trying to help, but pretty soon, my whole self-image was wrapped up in being victimized by that horrible man Andy." Betty had an "aha moment" when she understood that she was wallowing in her victim mentality, almost enjoying it. As is true so many times, once she realized this, she was able to journal about it and become aware of when her thoughts started to go down that "poor me" path.

By now, you should be feeling like you are traveling with a lighter load. You have done extensive work in identifying and expressing your feelings and needs, both in writing and to a confidante. You have changed viewpoints by walking a mile in the shoes of the other person, and you have gained perspective by getting out of your skin and viewing this incident and your life from a big-picture viewpoint.

Are you ready to let go of your feelings of anger, revenge, resentment, and hurt? In this step, consider the possibility of letting go of some of these dark emotions, and then act to release yourself from this negativity.

Exercise: Entertaining the possibility of letting go

At this point, let's examine your readiness and ability to release some of the anger, fear, or resentment you might feel about the grievance story. You might be clinging to several reasons not to let go. For example, perhaps you are receiving some sympathy from others when you reveal your grievance story. Or perhaps you have tied your self-image and self-worth to being the victim in your grievance story. You might feel superior over the other person as long as you retain the essence of the grievance story.

Are there any good reasons to hold on to your grievance story and all its negative emotions? Is there some benefit you would lose if you were to let go of your negative emotions about this?

_____

_____

_____

_____

_____

It is important to define a benefit for the process of forgiveness. When you get stuck in righteous feelings of being a victim, it is hard to imagine letting them go. However, a lot of mental and emotional energy goes into keeping your grievance story alive. Let's consider the benefits of not having the negative feelings and thoughts.

How would it feel if you could let go of your residual feelings and thoughts about the situation? How would you benefit from releasing your feelings about it?

_____

_____

_____

_____

_____

_____

_____

Exercise: Releasing emotions

In this exercise, there are three kinds of experiential techniques to help you let go of feelings that you hold onto about the grievance.

Human beings typically have a preferred way of learning and communicating. Researchers have grouped these learning preferences into the three major categories of visual, auditory, and kinesthetic. Although there are times when you use all three learning styles, typically one is used most often. Try to identify which learning style comes naturally to you as you read the following descriptions.

Visual learners prefer to read while learning, and tend to love graphs, pictures, maps, and other visual depictions of the material. They generally communicate best with visual presentations and visual language. Of the three categories, this is the most common.

Auditory learners learn best through hearing someone talk. They are great at listening to a lecture or a CD recording to understand a topic. They are typically sensitive to auditory distractions and appreciate music.

Kinesthetic learners prefer hands-on experiences when learning. They need to take something apart or at least touch it to understand it. They thrive on tactile experiences, roleplays, and just experimenting.

Each style has different ways of learning, thinking, and expressing their thoughts and feelings. At this point in the forgiveness process, you need to have tools to release any residual thoughts and feelings that you have about the grievance. Here are some letting go exercises for each of these learning preferences. Choose the method that speaks to you—or try them all!

Visual:

1. Imagine a rope tied in a knot, which represents the feelings you have about the grievance. Imagine that knot slowly unraveling as the rope comes apart strand by strand, until all that is left is a pile of hemp on the floor.

2. Mentally picture your emotions trapped in an automobile tire. Picture the air being slowly let out of the tire, until the tire is completely flat.

Auditory:

1. In a private room, take a deep breath and loudly say the sound "Ahhhhh" as you exhale. Imagine your emotions being released as the sound fades away.

2. Again in a private room, take a deep breath and forcefully yell the sound "arghhhhhh." Take another deep breath and say "ahhhhhh" in a normal voice. Take a last deep breath and softly hum "mmmmm." Imagine your emotions diminishing as you go through the exercise.

Kinesthetic:

1. Make a fist with your hand and squeeze it tightly for a minute or so. Gradually release your fist and slowly open your fingers, releasing your feelings as you do so.

2. Place both hands on your heart. Inhale deeply, pressing hands firmly on your heart. As you exhale, wipe your heart area with both hands as if you are wiping crumbs off a table, ending with a sweeping gesture into the air. Repeat this gesture several times as you imagine feelings being cleared out of your heart.

Betty reported that she is a visual learner and benefited most from the inflated tire image. She imagined her hurt and angry feelings filling up a big tractor tire, and then puncturing the tire with a sharp pick. Seeing the tire instantly deflate felt like a relief to her. But just for good measure, she added the sound of air quickly escaping from the tire—an auditory cue. "It made me feel really good to blow a raspberry with my lips as I imagined the air rushing out of the tire," she explained. "Somehow, including the sound made it real for me."

Describe the exercise you did and how you feel now:

_____

_____

_____

_____

_____

_____

_____

_____

Exercise: Forgiveness meditation or prayer

To help you let go, it is helpful to do a meditation or prayer in the style of the Buddhist practice of metta, or loving-kindness and compassion. Do not attempt this practice until you've gone through the previous steps and feel a reduced level of tension around the grievance story. If you haven't yet felt some release, this exercise will be very difficult and may even anger you.

In this exercise, you will first bless yourself, then the person who hurt you. Finally, you will bless both yourself and the other. You might wish to invite your Higher Power (whom you may call God, Yahweh, Goddess, Allah, Source, Beauty, or Love) to be the third person and witness to this event. For some, this sanctifies the prayer and grounds it in deep holiness.

For me, this was one of the final exercises I performed in forgiving a business partner who had left the partnership. As I imagined him sitting across from me, I could feel the goodness of this man's heart and all the conflict that he had felt. I asked the Divine to join us as our witness to this sacred act, and was comforted. In that holy moment, I knew at a soul level that my former partner knew he was forgiven and that he, in turn, forgave me.

Sit quietly, either in a chair where you can place your feet flat on the floor or on a meditation cushion or bench. You might light a candle as a symbol of your wish to burn off any negative energy. Sit up straight and take several deep, cleansing breaths to still your mind. When you feel centered and in the moment, imagine the person who hurt you sitting across from you. Look into that person's eyes, and then begin the prayer. Linger on each line, letting the essence of the words seep into your being. Breathe in and out several times as you contemplate the line. Then move on to the next line, working steadily through the prayer until you have finished. Then, honor yourself, honor your Higher Power, and honor the person who hurt you.

May I be at peace.

May my heart remain open.

May I awaken to my inner Divine essence.

May I be healed.

May I be a source of healing for all beings.

May You be at peace.

May Your heart remain open.

May You awaken to your inner Divine essence.

May You be healed.

May You be a source of healing for all beings.

May We be at peace.

May our hearts remain open.

May We awaken to our inner Divine essence.

May We be healed.

May We be a source of healing for all beings.

WRITE FORGIVENESS LETTERS

In the following exercises, you will write letters to the two important people in your grievance story: the person who hurt you and yourself. You will remember the benefits of writing about important emotional issues and how the act of writing brings your emotions into the analytical portion of the brain. Writing also converts thoughts to a small action, which advances the process of manifesting the outcome you dream for.

The significance of writing forgiveness letters is huge. Writing converts your forgiveness emotions to a tangible, earthly form. It commits you in a way that mere thoughts or spoken words cannot. That is why you record important commitments in the form of written contracts. The forgiveness letters that you are about to write are like heavenly contracts that bind your heart.

The magic of these letters is in the writing, not the sending. This is good news if the person you need to forgive is no longer alive, but is also beneficial if you feel no need to confront the person who hurt you. Remember, it is OK to decide that there is no place for that person in your current and future life.

If you decide not to send the letter or communicate with the other person in your grievance story, you might wish to communicate your forgiveness through a means that I call "Heavenly Instant Messaging" or HIM. It's easy to do HIM. Just quiet your mind by relaxing your body and taking several deep breaths. Picture in your mind the face of the person you wish to forgive. Feel your heart fill with compassion and forgiveness for that person. Then mentally imagine a spiritual broadband Internet connection up to heaven and then back down to the other person. The reason you connect through heaven is to consecrate the connection and to add the power of the angels and the Divine to the communication. Once you feel that the heavenly broadband connection is working, pulse compassion and forgiveness over the connection, through heaven, and on to the other person. Reverse the pulse and send forgiveness back to yourself. Know that in this act of heartfelt forgiveness, the other person is receiving that message on a soul level. Both souls are forgiven.

Exercise: Write a forgiveness letter

Write a forgiveness letter to the person who hurt you, acknowledging the emotions that person might have felt, what their needs might have been, and what elements of their background might explain their actions.

Exercise: Write a forgiveness letter to yourself

Write yourself a forgiveness letter. Acknowledge your feelings, your needs, and what elements of your background explain your actions or lack thereof. Write of your pride in the good work you've done in this journal, and forgive yourself for whatever you feel guilty or regretful about in the grievance story. Know that heaven joins you in forgiving yourself, and that you bask in the Divine's unending forgiveness, love, and acceptance of you, just as you are. You can write here in your journal, or you can compose it on stationery, in which case you will self-address the envelope, stamp it, and mail it.

Several months ago, I wrote myself a forgiveness note and mailed it via U.S. mail. When it arrived two days later, I treated it in the same way dogs bury a bone so they can chew on it later. I placed the unopened letter on my meditation cushion and waited until my evening prayer time to read it. Then I savored the letter by reading it several times, letting the words soak into the center of my soul. I cherish that letter, keeping it next to my meditation cushion and re-reading it every so often to remind me of the good work I did.

_____

_____

_____

_____

_____

_____

_____

_____

_____

_____

_____

_____

CHAPTER EIGHT
Step Six: Take Action

Betty was in a quandary. She had re-paid tens of thousands of dollars of credit card debt that her ex-husband had not revealed during either their marriage or the divorce proceedings. Tallying her total financial burden, she decided it was worthwhile to take Andy back to court to see if she could get him to pay some of his own debt. After over a year of attorney's meetings, court dates, and mountains of paperwork to back up her claims, she received a ruling in her favor. Her ex-husband's wages were garnished to pay for a substantial portion of the financial burden she had assumed after the divorce."

Betty remarked about the process in this way. "If I hadn't done all the inner work on my emotions and anger toward Andy—if I hadn't really forgiven him for being dishonest to me and ruining my credit—I wouldn't have had the emotional stamina to take the legal proceeding to the end. I needed to clear all that excess baggage that I was carrying—the negative victim mentality—to allow me to stand up for myself and take legal action. He paid the natural consequence for his dishonesty."

Now that your energy is clear, you can take action. Remember that forgiveness does not mean that you protect the other person from the natural consequences of their actions. But now that you've lightened your load of negative feelings and have blessed the other person, you will think more clearly in order to decide on the appropriate action to take.

Depending on the specifics of your situation, you might:

- Talk to the person who hurt you. Express to them that you've forgiven them.

- Mail your forgiveness letter and let it speak for you. You may need to prepare for some further communication from the person who hurt you, or you can make it clear in your letter that you do not wish to have any further communication.

- Burn the letter and do not send it. Heaven knows the workings of your heart, and will send your forgiveness to the soul of the other person via what I call Soul Mail. On a spiritual level, the other person will know that you have forgiven.

- Take legal action. If the nature of the grievance was a breach of the law, it is appropriate to seek legal assistance and pursue legal action. There may be a moral or legal imperative to do so, if you perceive that you must stop the other person from repeating their actions on others. This is especially true in abuse cases.

- Seek reparations of some sort. The situation might be a neighborhood youth who broke a window in your home, or the employer who didn't pay you properly. You may need to negotiate with the person who hurt you to seek amends for what happened.

Plan your next action and notate it here:

_____

_____

_____

_____

_____

_____

_____

_____

_____

....
Take
Action

CHAPTER NINE
Step Seven: Bless the Other

Both Betty and Jay had a very hard time forgiving. They had suffered greatly because of their grievance story. Perhaps because his father was now deceased, Jay had an easier time with this final step. "Now, when I think of my dad," says Jay, "I can feel empathy for him and the abuse he suffered during the war. Sometimes I can even bless him. It's really nice that my brain doesn't automatically go to angry thoughts about Dad anymore—I used to feel like a rat on an exercise wheel, never getting anywhere. Now I can choose what to think when a memory of him comes up."

Betty, on the other hand, still has trouble with this last step. "I'm working on it, really I am," she confesses. "But I just can't bless Andy yet. I guess I'm just still too close to the situation. Instead of blessing him when I think of him, I try to think of him as just another soul, doing the best he can with where he is. Sometimes that helps."

Your brain is accustomed to thinking negative thoughts about this situation. Once you have discharged most of your anger or dark emotions, you can re-train your brain to take a different path when you happen to think of this person. Whenever you think of the other, instead of re-playing your grievance story and emotional reactions, take a deep breath and bless the person. You might use one of the following phrases:

- "Bless you"

- "I wish you well"

- "Namaste"

- "I honor your true essence"

This step requires constant monitoring of your thoughts, especially during the first few days. But research has shown that twenty-one days of practicing a new thought pattern will create a new neural pathway in your brain. You will then be on your way to complete freedom from the prison in which unforgiveness had you jailed.

What is the blessing you will repeat when you happen to think of your grievance story?

_____

_____

_____

_____

_____

_____

Exercise: The burning bowl

You may wish to perform a private burning ceremony to symbolize your letting go of a past situation and the pain it caused you. You might wish to ceremonially burn pages 11 and 12 of this manual, which is the record of your feelings about the situation, or create another visual image on paper of what you wish to release from your consciousness.

Choose a safe place such as a well-vented fireplace or outside grill to burn the papers.

I once did this by burning pages from my journal in our outside grill. I reverently watched the pages turn black and shrivel up. Then

I scattered the burnt ashes in my yard, releasing all my negative thoughts to the wind.

How did you feel after your burning ceremony?

_____

_____

_____

_____

_____

_____

CONGRATULATIONS!

It may take you days, months, or years to lighten your load of feelings of unforgiveness, but with patience, you will be traveling lighter soon. You may need to repeat some of the steps in this journal, like writing expressively about your thoughts and feelings. Be assured that with each effort you make, you will reap the benefits of your good work. Be easy on yourself, and celebrate each baby step that you take.

I know from personal experience that life is much easier when you have forgiven others and yourself. You free up reserves of energy that had formerly been spent on re-playing your grievance story and stoking the fire of your emotions. Now you are free to spend that energy on happier and more productive endeavors.

● ● ●

Bless
The
Other

Part Three

More Forgiveness Opportunities

IN PART TWO, YOU HAVE six more opportunities to work through grievances. Although the detailed explanations are not repeated, the forgiveness exercises are. Page references to detailed descriptions of the exercises in Part One are included in several places.

Blessings to you as you continue on your journey toward wholeness, using the power of forgiveness!

CHAPTER TEN
Forgiveness Opportunity Two

STEP ONE: IDENTIFY YOUR FEELINGS

Briefly describe the grievance story you wish to work on here:

_____

_____

_____

_____

_____

_____

Exercise: Identify your feelings

When you think of your forgiveness opportunity, what are the primary emotions that you feel? Please refer to the list on page 33.

_____

_____

_____

_____

_____

_____

What were your unmet needs in the situation? Please refer to the list of human needs on page 35.

_____

_____

_____

_____

_____

Now, please write for about ten minutes about your deepest thoughts and emotions about your forgiveness opportunity. If you begin to feel a strong emotion, stay with it but try to observe it from an objective point of view. As you observe it in this manner, its intensity will fade.

The objective in this exercise is to notate your feelings and thoughts expressively as possible. Do not hold back on your emotions.

_____

_____

_____

_____

STEP TWO: TALK IT OUT

Exercise: Talking it out

At some point, you may wish to share your forgiveness opportunity story with a friend, partner, or confidante.

Describe how your talk went and how you felt after it:

_____

_____

_____

_____

_____

_____

STEP THREE: CHANGE VIEWPOINTS

Exercise: Change viewpoints

Think about your grievance story and what you knew about the other person. What might have been going on in his life that made him act the way he did? For example, if your grievance story involves a parent, write about what aspects of her upbringing or the difficulties she was grappling with at the time of your story.

Or you can ask yourself, what would cause me to act this way? What could have happened to me to motivate me to do the same? What in my history, my beliefs, the way my parents raised me, the traumas, etc. might have caused me to be like the other person?

_____

_____

_____

_____

Were there some challenges or difficulties she was facing? What else might he have been dealing with that you weren't aware of? What emotions might the other person have felt? Please refer to the list of emotions on page 33. What were the other person's needs? Please refer to the list of human needs on page 35. Take time to write about what the other person might have been feeling and what his needs were:

_____

_____

_____

_____

_____

_____

Exercise: Taking responsibility for your part

What did you do to contribute to the situation? In every situation, there is something—some action that you took or didn't take—that you feel responsible for. This is an accountability step, and it also identifies what you may need to forgive in yourself.

_____

_____

_____

_____

I wish to forgive myself for the part I took in creating this grievance. Specifically, I wish to forgive myself for:

_____

_____

_____

_____

_____

_____

_____

_____

_____

_____

_____

STEP FOUR: GAIN PERSPECTIVE

Exercise: Newspaper reporter

Pretend you are a newspaper reporter and write a short article about your forgiveness opportunity. Use the third person, and include only the facts (who, what, where, when, how).

_____

_____

_____

_____

_____

_____

_____

_____

_____

_____

_____

Exercise: The wide-angle lens

What were the positive aspects or results of the situation?
Did you learn something, develop skills; what gifts did you
receive because of this? If sufficient time has not passed for
this to become evident, imagine what benefits might come
from this situation.

_____

_____

_____

_____

_____

_____

Exercise: The deathbed exercise

What will you remember of this at the end of your life?
Will you even remember it? How?

_____

_____

_____

_____

_____

Exercise: The heavenly perspective

Sit quietly in your chair and either close your eyes or
soft-focus them on a spot on the floor. Relax your body and
take a deep breath.

Imagine yourself in your grievance story, with all of its
problems, dark emotions, and difficulties. Picture a scene
that represents the issues you are grappling with and picture
yourself in the scene. What are you doing, feeling, and saying?

Once you get a clear picture of this scene, make a clone of your spirit and assign it the job of "observer." Make your observer spirit fly up to the rooftop to view this scene with your spirit's X-ray vision. What do you observe from the rooftop?

_____

_____

_____

_____

Now send your spirit up to the clouds and have it view the scene with you in it. What does your spirit observe from the clouds?

_____

_____

_____

_____

Now send your spirit up to the moon and have it view the scene with you in it. What does your spirit observe from the moon?

_____

_____

_____

_____

Now send your spirit up to heaven, where it can perceive all of the cosmos. Ask your spirit to view the scene back on earth. Then tell your spirit to consult with a Divine entity (you might call it God, Goddess, Allah, or others) to determine if there is a Divine meaning to what is going on in the scene on earth. Listen closely and note what your spirit tells you from heaven.

_____

_____

_____

_____

Come back to earth and slowly open your eyes. Breathe deeply.

Exercise: The hero perspective

In order to turn around a grievance story, you need to paint yourself as the hero in the story. Focus on the amazing resilience you showed—after all, you survived, didn't you? How were you the hero in this story?

_____

_____

_____

_____

_____

_____

_____

_____

_____

_____

_____

_____

_____

_____

_____

_____

STEP FIVE: LETTING GO

Exercise: Entertaining the possibility of letting go

Are there any good reasons to hold on to your grievance story and all its negative emotions? Is there some benefit you would lose if you were to let go of your negative emotions about this?

_____

_____

_____

_____

_____

It is important to define a benefit for the process of forgiveness. When you get stuck in righteous feelings of being a victim, it is hard to imagine letting them go. However, a lot of mental and emotional energy goes into keeping your grievance story alive. Let's consider the benefits of not having the negative feelings and thoughts.

How would it feel if you could let go of your residual feelings and thoughts about the situation? How would you benefit from releasing your feelings about it?

_____

_____

_____

_____

_____

_____

_____

Exercise: Releasing emotions

Review the visual, auditory and kinesthetic letting go exercises found on pages 60-61.

Describe the exercise you did and how you feel now:

_____

_____

_____

_____

_____

Exercise: Forgiveness meditation or prayer

May I be at peace.

May my heart remain open.

May I awaken to my inner Divine essence.

May I be healed.

May I be a source of healing for all beings.

May You be at peace.

May Your heart remain open.

May You awaken to your inner Divine essence.

May You be healed.

May You be a source of healing for all beings.

May We be at peace.

May our hearts remain open.

May We awaken to our inner Divine essence.

May We be healed.

May We be a source of healing for all beings.

Exercise: Write a forgiveness letter

Write a forgiveness letter to the person who hurt you, acknowledging the emotions that person might have felt, what their needs might have been, and what elements of their background might explain their actions.

_____

_____

_____

_____

_____

_____

_____

_____

_____

_____

_____

_____

_____

_____

_____

_____

_____

_____

_____

_____

_____

_____

_____

93
....

Forgiveness
Opportunity
Two

Exercise: Write a forgiveness letter to yourself

Write yourself a forgiveness letter. Acknowledge your
feelings, your needs and what elements of your background
explain your actions or lack thereof. Write of your pride in the
good work you've done in this journal, and forgive yourself
for whatever you feel guilty or regretful about in the grievance
story. Know that heaven joins you in forgiving yourself, and
that you bask in the Divine's unending forgiveness, love and
acceptance of you, just as you are. You can write here in your
journal, or you can compose it on stationery, in which case you
will self-address the envelope, stamp it and mail it.

STEP SIX: TAKE ACTION

Plan your next action and notate it here:

_____

_____

_____

_____

_____

_____

STEP SEVEN: BLESS THE OTHER

What is the blessing you will repeat when you happen to think of your grievance story?

_____

_____

_____

_____

_____

_____

CHAPTER ELEVEN
Forgiveness Opportunity Three

STEP ONE: IDENTIFY YOUR FEELINGS

Briefly describe the grievance story you wish to work on here:

_____

_____

_____

_____

_____

_____

Exercise: Identify your feelings

When you think of your forgiveness opportunity, what are the primary emotions that you feel? Please refer to the list on page 33.

_____

_____

_____

_____

_____

_____

What were your unmet needs in the situation? Please refer to the list of human needs on page 35.

_____

_____

_____

_____

_____

_____

Now, please write for about ten minutes about your deepest thoughts and emotions about your forgiveness opportunity. If you begin to feel a strong emotion, stay with it but try to observe it from an objective point of view. As you observe it in this manner, its intensity will fade.

The objective in this exercise is to notate your feelings and thoughts expressively as possible. Do not hold back on your emotions.

_____

_____

_____

_____

STEP TWO: TALK IT OUT

Exercise: Talking it out

At some point, you may wish to share your forgiveness opportunity story with a friend, partner, or confidante.

Describe how your talk went and how you felt after it:

_____

_____

_____

_____

_____

_____

STEP THREE: CHANGE VIEWPOINTS

Exercise: Change viewpoints

Think about your grievance story and what you knew about the other person. What might have been going on in his life that made him act the way he did? For example, if your grievance story involves a parent, write about what aspects of her upbringing or the difficulties she was grappling with at the time of your story.

Or you can ask yourself, what would cause me to act this way? What could have happened to me to motivate me to do the same? What in my history, my beliefs, the way my parents raised me, the traumas, etc. might have caused me to be like the other person?

_____

_____

_____

_____

Were there some challenges or difficulties she was facing? What else might he have been dealing with that you weren't aware of? What emotions might the other person have felt? Please refer to the list of emotions on page 33. What were the other person's needs? Please refer to the list of human needs on page 35. Take time to write about what the other person might have been feeling and what his needs were:

_____

_____

_____

_____

_____

Exercise: Taking responsibility for your part

What did you do to contribute to the situation? In every situation, there is something—some action that you took or didn't take—that you feel responsible for. This is an accountability step, and it also identifies what you may need to forgive in yourself.

_____

_____

_____

_____

I wish to forgive myself for the part I took in creating this grievance. Specifically, I wish to forgive myself for:

_____

_____

_____

_____

_____

_____

_____

_____

_____

_____

_____

STEP FOUR: GAIN PERSPECTIVE

Exercise: Newspaper reporter

Pretend you are a newspaper reporter and write a short article about your forgiveness opportunity. Use the third person, and include only the facts (who, what, where, when, how).

Forgiveness Opportunity Three

_____

_____

_____

_____

_____

_____

_____

_____

_____

_____

_____

_____

Exercise: The wide-angle lens

What were the positive aspects or results of the situation? Did you learn something, develop skills; what gifts did you receive because of this? If sufficient time has not passed for this to become evident, imagine what benefits might come from this situation.

_____

_____

_____

_____

_____

_____

Exercise: The deathbed exercise

What will you remember of this at the end of your life? Will you even remember it? How?

_____

_____

_____

_____

_____

Exercise: The heavenly perspective

Sit quietly in your chair and either close your eyes or soft-focus them on a spot on the floor. Relax your body and take a deep breath.

Imagine yourself in your grievance story, with all of its problems, dark emotions, and difficulties. Picture a scene that represents the issues you are grappling with and picture yourself in the scene. What are you doing, feeling, and saying?

Once you get a clear picture of this scene, make a clone of your spirit and assign it the job of "observer." Make your observer spirit fly up to the rooftop to view this scene with your spirit's X-ray vision. What do you observe from the rooftop?

_____

_____

_____

_____

Now send your spirit up to the clouds and have it view the scene with you in it. What does your spirit observe from the clouds?

_____

_____

_____

_____

Now send your spirit up to the moon and have it view the scene with you in it. What does your spirit observe from the moon?

_____

_____

_____

_____

Now send your spirit up to heaven, where it can perceive all of the cosmos. Ask your spirit to view the scene back on earth. Then tell your spirit to consult with a Divine entity (you might call it God, Goddess, Allah, or others) to determine if there is a Divine meaning to what is going on in the scene on earth. Listen closely and note what your spirit tells you from heaven.

_____

_____

_____

_____

Come back to earth and slowly open your eyes. Breathe deeply.

Exercise: The hero perspective

In order to turn around a grievance story, you need to paint yourself as the hero in the story. Focus on the amazing resilience you showed—after all, you survived, didn't you? How were you the hero in this story?

_____

_____

_____

_____

_____

_____

_____

_____

_____

_____

_____

_____

_____

_____

_____

_____

_____

_____

_____

STEP FIVE: LETTING GO

Exercise: Entertaining the possibility of letting go

Are there any good reasons to hold on to your grievance story and all its negative emotions? Is there some benefit you would lose if you were to let go of your negative emotions about this?

_____

_____

_____

_____

_____

_____

It is important to define a benefit for the process of forgiveness. When you get stuck in righteous feelings of being a victim, it is hard to imagine letting them go. However, a lot of mental and emotional energy goes into keeping your grievance story alive. Let's consider the benefits of not having the negative feelings and thoughts.

How would it feel if you could let go of your residual feelings and thoughts about the situation? How would you benefit from releasing your feelings about it?

_____

_____

_____

_____

_____

_____

_____

_____

Forgiveness
Opportunity
Three

Exercise: Releasing emotions

Review the visual, auditory and kinesthetic letting go exercises found on pages 60-61.

Describe the exercise you did and how you feel now:

_____

_____

_____

_____

_____

_____

Exercise: Forgiveness meditation or prayer

May I be at peace.

May my heart remain open.

May I awaken to my inner Divine essence.

May I be healed.

May I be a source of healing for all beings.

May You be at peace.

May Your heart remain open.

May You awaken to your inner Divine essence.

May You be healed.

May You be a source of healing for all beings.

May We be at peace.

May our hearts remain open.

May We awaken to our inner Divine essence.

May We be healed.

May We be a source of healing for all beings.

Exercise: Write a forgiveness letter

Write a forgiveness letter to the person who hurt you, acknowledging the emotions that person might have felt, what their needs might have been, and what elements of their background might explain their actions.

_____

_____

_____

_____

_____

_____

_____

_____

_____

_____

_____

_____

_____

_____

_____

_____

_____

_____

_____

_____

109

. . . .

Forgiveness
Opportunity
Three

Exercise: Write a forgiveness letter to yourself

Write yourself a forgiveness letter. Acknowledge your feelings, your needs and what elements of your background explain your actions or lack thereof. Write of your pride in the good work you've done in this journal, and forgive yourself for whatever you feel guilty or regretful about in the grievance story. Know that heaven joins you in forgiving yourself, and that you bask in the Divine's unending forgiveness, love and acceptance of you, just as you are. You can write here in your journal, or you can compose it on stationery, in which case you will self-address the envelope, stamp it and mail it.

STEP SIX: TAKE ACTION

Plan your next action and notate it here:

_____

_____

_____

_____

_____

_____

STEP SEVEN: BLESS THE OTHER

What is the blessing you will repeat when you happen to think of your grievance story?

_____

_____

_____

_____

_____

_____

CHAPTER TWELVE
Forgiveness Opportunity Four

STEP ONE: IDENTIFY YOUR FEELINGS

Briefly describe the grievance story you wish to work on here:

_____

_____

_____

_____

_____

_____

Exercise: Identify your feelings

When you think of your forgiveness opportunity, what are the primary emotions that you feel? Please refer to the list on page 33.

_____

_____

_____

_____

_____

_____

What were your unmet needs in the situation? Please refer to the list of human needs on page 35.

_____

_____

_____

_____

_____

Now, please write for about ten minutes about your deepest thoughts and emotions about your forgiveness opportunity. If you begin to feel a strong emotion, stay with it but try to observe it from an objective point of view. As you observe it in this manner, its intensity will fade.

The objective in this exercise is to notate your feelings and thoughts expressively as possible. Do not hold back on your emotions.

_____

_____

_____

_____

STEP TWO: TALK IT OUT

Exercise: Talking it out

At some point, you may wish to share your forgiveness opportunity story with a friend, partner, or confidante.

Describe how your talk went and how you felt after it:

_____

_____

_____

_____

_____

_____

STEP THREE: CHANGE VIEWPOINTS

Exercise: Change viewpoints

Think about your grievance story and what you knew about the other person. What might have been going on in his life that made him act the way he did? For example, if your grievance story involves a parent, write about what aspects of her upbringing or the difficulties she was grappling with at the time of your story.

Or you can ask yourself, what would cause me to act this way? What could have happened to me to motivate me to do the same? What in my history, my beliefs, the way my parents raised me, the traumas, etc. might have caused me to be like the other person?

_____

_____

_____

_____

_____

_____

Were there some challenges or difficulties she was facing? What else might he have been dealing with that you weren't aware of? What emotions might the other person have felt? Please refer to the list of emotions on page 33. What were the other person's needs? Please refer to the list of human needs on page 35. Take time to write about what the other person might have been feeling and what his needs were:

_____

_____

_____

_____

_____

Exercise: Taking responsibility for your part

What did you do to contribute to the situation? In every situation, there is something—some action that you took or didn't take—that you feel responsible for. This is an accountability step, and it also identifies what you may need to forgive in yourself.

_____

_____

_____

_____

I wish to forgive myself for the part I took in creating this grievance. Specifically, I wish to forgive myself for:

_____

_____

_____

_____

_____

_____

_____

_____

_____

_____

_____

_____

STEP FOUR: GAIN PERSPECTIVE

Exercise: Newspaper reporter

Pretend you are a newspaper reporter and write a short article about your forgiveness opportunity. Use the third person, and include only the facts (who, what, where, when, how).

_____

_____

_____

_____

_____

_____

_____

_____

_____

_____

_____

Exercise: The wide-angle lens

What were the positive aspects or results of the situation?
Did you learn something, develop skills; what gifts did you
receive because of this? If sufficient time has not passed for
this to become evident, imagine what benefits might come
from this situation.

_____

_____

_____

_____

_____

_____

Exercise: The deathbed exercise

What will you remember of this at the end of your life?
Will you even remember it? How?

_____

_____

_____

_____

_____

_____

Exercise: The heavenly perspective

Sit quietly in your chair and either close your eyes or
soft-focus them on a spot on the floor. Relax your body and
take a deep breath.

Imagine yourself in your grievance story, with all of its
problems, dark emotions, and difficulties. Picture a scene
that represents the issues you are grappling with and picture
yourself in the scene. What are you doing, feeling, and saying?

Once you get a clear picture of this scene, make a clone of your spirit and assign it the job of "observer." Make your observer spirit fly up to the rooftop to view this scene with your spirit's X-ray vision. What do you observe from the rooftop?

_____

_____

_____

_____

Now send your spirit up to the clouds and have it view the scene with you in it. What does your spirit observe from the clouds?

_____

_____

_____

_____

Now send your spirit up to the moon and have it view the scene with you in it. What does your spirit observe from the moon?

_____

_____

_____

_____

Now send your spirit up to heaven, where it can perceive all of the cosmos. Ask your spirit to view the scene back on earth. Then tell your spirit to consult with a Divine entity (you might call it God, Goddess, Allah, or others) to determine if there is a Divine meaning to what is going on in the scene on earth. Listen closely and note what your spirit tells you from heaven.

_____

_____

_____

_____

Come back to earth and slowly open your eyes. Breathe deeply.

Exercise: The hero perspective

In order to turn around a grievance story, you need to paint yourself as the hero in the story. Focus on the amazing resilience you showed—after all, you survived, didn't you? How were you the hero in this story?

_____

_____

_____

_____

_____

_____

_____

_____

_____

_____

_____

_____

_____

_____

_____

_____

_____

_____

_____

STEP FIVE: LETTING GO

Exercise: Entertaining the possibility of letting go

Are there any good reasons to hold on to your grievance story and all its negative emotions? Is there some benefit you would lose if you were to let go of your negative emotions about this?

_____

_____

_____

_____

_____

_____

It is important to define a benefit for the process of forgiveness. When you get stuck in righteous feelings of being a victim, it is hard to imagine letting them go. However, a lot of mental and emotional energy goes into keeping your grievance story alive. Let's consider the benefits of not having the negative feelings and thoughts.

How would it feel if you could let go of your residual feelings and thoughts about the situation? How would you benefit from releasing your feelings about it?

_____

_____

_____

_____

_____

_____

_____

_____

Exercise: Releasing emotions

Review the visual, auditory and kinesthetic letting go exercises found on pages 60-61.

Describe the exercise you did and how you feel now:

_____

_____

_____

_____

_____

_____

Exercise: Forgiveness meditation or prayer

May I be at peace.

May my heart remain open.

May I awaken to my inner Divine essence.

May I be healed.

May I be a source of healing for all beings.

May You be at peace.

May Your heart remain open.

May You awaken to your inner Divine essence.

May You be healed.

May You be a source of healing for all beings.

May We be at peace.

May our hearts remain open.

May We awaken to our inner Divine essence.

May We be healed.

May We be a source of healing for all beings.

Exercise: Write a forgiveness letter

Write a forgiveness letter to the person who hurt you, acknowledging the emotions that person might have felt, what their needs might have been, and what elements of their background might explain their actions.

_____

_____

_____

_____

_____

_____

_____

_____

125

. . . .

_____

Forgiveness

_____

Opportunity

_____

Four

_____

_____

_____

_____

_____

_____

_____

_____

Exercise: Write a forgiveness letter to yourself

Write yourself a forgiveness letter. Acknowledge your feelings, your needs and what elements of your background explain your actions or lack thereof. Write of your pride in the good work you've done in this journal, and forgive yourself for whatever you feel guilty or regretful about in the grievance story. Know that heaven joins you in forgiving yourself, and that you bask in the Divine's unending forgiveness, love and acceptance of you, just as you are. You can write here in your journal, or you can compose it on stationery, in which case you will self-address the envelope, stamp it and mail it.

STEP SIX: TAKE ACTION

Plan your next action and notate it here:

_____

_____

_____

_____

_____

_____

STEP SEVEN: BLESS THE OTHER

What is the blessing you will repeat when you happen to think of your grievance story?

_____

_____

_____

_____

_____

_____

● ● ●

CHAPTER THIRTEEN
Forgiveness Opportunity Five

STEP ONE: IDENTIFY YOUR FEELINGS

Briefly describe the grievance story you wish to work on here:

_____

_____

_____

_____

_____

_____

Exercise: Identify your feelings

When you think of your forgiveness opportunity, what are the primary emotions that you feel? Please refer to the list on page 33.

_____

_____

_____

_____

_____

What were your unmet needs in the situation? Please refer to the list of human needs on page 35.

_____

_____

_____

_____

_____

Now, please write for about ten minutes about your deepest thoughts and emotions about your forgiveness opportunity. If you begin to feel a strong emotion, stay with it but try to observe it from an objective point of view. As you observe it in this manner, its intensity will fade.

The objective in this exercise is to notate your feelings and thoughts expressively as possible. Do not hold back on your emotions.

_____

_____

_____

_____

STEP TWO: TALK IT OUT

Exercise: Talking it out

At some point, you may wish to share your forgiveness opportunity story with a friend, partner, or confidante.

Describe how your talk went and how you felt after it:

_____

_____

_____

_____

_____

_____

STEP THREE: CHANGE VIEWPOINTS

Exercise: Change viewpoints

Think about your grievance story and what you knew about the other person. What might have been going on in his life that made him act the way he did? For example, if your grievance story involves a parent, write about what aspects of her upbringing or the difficulties she was grappling with at the time of your story.

Or you can ask yourself, what would cause me to act this way? What could have happened to me to motivate me to do the same? What in my history, my beliefs, the way my parents raised me, the traumas, etc. might have caused me to be like the other person?

_____

_____

_____

_____

_____

_____

Were there some challenges or difficulties she was facing? What else might he have been dealing with that you weren't aware of? What emotions might the other person have felt? Please refer to the list of emotions on page 33. What were the other person's needs? Please refer to the list of human needs on page 35. Take time to write about what the other person might have been feeling and what his needs were:

_____

_____

_____

_____

_____

_____

Exercise: Taking responsibility for your part

What did you do to contribute to the situation? In every situation, there is something—some action that you took or didn't take—that you feel responsible for. This is an accountability step, and it also identifies what you may need to forgive in yourself.

_____

_____

_____

_____

I wish to forgive myself for the part I took in creating this grievance. Specifically, I wish to forgive myself for:

_____

_____

_____

_____

_____

_____

_____

_____

_____

_____

_____

STEP FOUR: GAIN PERSPECTIVE

Exercise: Newspaper reporter

Pretend you are a newspaper reporter and write a short article about your forgiveness opportunity. Use the third person, and include only the facts (who, what, where, when, how).

_____

_____

_____

_____

_____

_____

_____

_____

_____

_____

_____

_____

Exercise: The wide-angle lens

What were the positive aspects or results of the situation? Did you learn something, develop skills; what gifts did you receive because of this? If sufficient time has not passed for this to become evident, imagine what benefits might come from this situation.

_____

_____

_____

_____

_____

_____

....

Exercise: The deathbed exercise

What will you remember of this at the end of your life? Will you even remember it? How?

_____

_____

_____

_____

_____

Exercise: The heavenly perspective

Sit quietly in your chair and either close your eyes or soft-focus them on a spot on the floor. Relax your body and take a deep breath.

Imagine yourself in your grievance story, with all of its problems, dark emotions, and difficulties. Picture a scene that represents the issues you are grappling with and picture yourself in the scene. What are you doing, feeling, and saying?

Once you get a clear picture of this scene, make a clone of your spirit and assign it the job of "observer." Make your observer spirit fly up to the rooftop to view this scene with your spirit's X-ray vision. What do you observe from the rooftop?

_____

_____

_____

_____

Now send your spirit up to the clouds and have it view the scene with you in it. What does your spirit observe from the clouds?

_____

_____

_____

_____

Now send your spirit up to the moon and have it view the scene with you in it. What does your spirit observe from the moon?

_____

_____

_____

_____

Now send your spirit up to heaven, where it can perceive all of the cosmos. Ask your spirit to view the scene back on earth. Then tell your spirit to consult with a Divine entity (you might call it God, Goddess, Allah, or others) to determine if there is a Divine meaning to what is going on in the scene on earth. Listen closely and note what your spirit tells you from heaven.

_____

_____

_____

_____

Come back to earth and slowly open your eyes. Breathe deeply.

Exercise: The hero perspective

In order to turn around a grievance story, you need to paint yourself as the hero in the story. Focus on the amazing resilience you showed—after all, you survived, didn't you? How were you the hero in this story?

STEP FIVE: LETTING GO

Exercise: Entertaining the possibility of letting go

Are there any good reasons to hold on to your grievance story and all its negative emotions? Is there some benefit you would lose if you were to let go of your negative emotions about this?

———————————————————————————

———————————————————————————

———————————————————————————

———————————————————————————

———————————————————————————

It is important to define a benefit for the process of forgiveness. When you get stuck in righteous feelings of being a victim, it is hard to imagine letting them go. However, a lot of mental and emotional energy goes into keeping your grievance story alive. Let's consider the benefits of not having the negative feelings and thoughts.

How would it feel if you could let go of your residual feelings and thoughts about the situation? How would you benefit from releasing your feelings about it?

———————————————————————————

———————————————————————————

———————————————————————————

———————————————————————————

———————————————————————————

———————————————————————————

———————————————————————————

Exercise: Releasing emotions

Review the visual, auditory and kinesthetic letting go exercises found on pages 60-61.

Describe the exercise you did and how you feel now:

_____

_____

_____

_____

_____

_____

Exercise: Forgiveness meditation or prayer

May I be at peace.

May my heart remain open.

May I awaken to my inner Divine essence.

May I be healed.

May I be a source of healing for all beings.

May You be at peace.

May Your heart remain open.

May You awaken to your inner Divine essence.

May You be healed.

May You be a source of healing for all beings.

May We be at peace.

May our hearts remain open.

May We awaken to our inner Divine essence.

May We be healed.

May We be a source of healing for all beings.

Exercise: Write a forgiveness letter

Write a forgiveness letter to the person who hurt you, acknowledging the emotions that person might have felt, what their needs might have been, and what elements of their background might explain their actions.

_____

_____

_____

_____

_____

_____

_____

_____

_____

_____

_____

141
....

Forgiveness
Opportunity
Five

_____

_____

_____

_____

_____

_____

_____

_____

_____

Exercise: Write a forgiveness letter to yourself

Write yourself a forgiveness letter. Acknowledge your feelings, your needs and what elements of your background explain your actions or lack thereof. Write of your pride in the good work you've done in this journal, and forgive yourself for whatever you feel guilty or regretful about in the grievance story. Know that heaven joins you in forgiving yourself, and that you bask in the Divine's unending forgiveness, love and acceptance of you, just as you are. You can write here in your journal, or you can compose it on stationery, in which case you will self-address the envelope, stamp it and mail it.

STEP SIX: TAKE ACTION

Plan your next action and notate it here:

_____

_____

_____

_____

_____

_____

STEP SEVEN: BLESS THE OTHER

What is the blessing you will repeat when you happen to think of your grievance story?

_____

_____

_____

_____

_____

● ● ●

CHAPTER FOURTEEN
Forgiveness Opportunity Six

STEP ONE: IDENTIFY YOUR FEELINGS

Briefly describe the grievance story you wish to work on here:

_____

_____

_____

_____

_____

_____

Exercise: Identify your feelings

When you think of your forgiveness opportunity, what are the primary emotions that you feel? Please refer to the list on page 33.

_____

_____

_____

_____

_____

_____

What were your unmet needs in the situation? Please refer to the list of human needs on page 35.

_____

_____

_____

_____

_____

_____

Now, please write for about ten minutes about your deepest thoughts and emotions about your forgiveness opportunity. If you begin to feel a strong emotion, stay with it but try to observe it from an objective point of view. As you observe it in this manner, its intensity will fade.

The objective in this exercise is to notate your feelings and thoughts expressively as possible. Do not hold back on your emotions.

_____

_____

_____

_____

_____

STEP TWO: TALK IT OUT

Exercise: Talking it out

At some point, you may wish to share your forgiveness opportunity story with a friend, partner, or confidante.

Describe how your talk went and how you felt after it:

STEP THREE: CHANGE VIEWPOINTS

Exercise: Change viewpoints

Think about your grievance story and what you knew about the other person. What might have been going on in his life that made him act the way he did? For example, if your grievance story involves a parent, write about what aspects of her upbringing or the difficulties she was grappling with at the time of your story.

Or you can ask yourself, what would cause me to act this way? What could have happened to me to motivate me to do the same? What in my history, my beliefs, the way my parents raised me, the traumas, etc. might have caused me to be like the other person?

Were there some challenges or difficulties she was facing?
What else might he have been dealing with that you weren't
aware of? What emotions might the other person have felt?
Please refer to the list of emotions on page 33. What were the
other person's needs? Please refer to the list of human needs
on page 35. Take time to write about what the other person
might have been feeling and what his needs were:

_____

_____

_____

_____

_____

_____

Exercise: Taking responsibility for your part

What did you do to contribute to the situation? In every
situation, there is something—some action that you took or
didn't take—that you feel responsible for. This is an account-
ability step, and it also identifies what you may need to forgive
in yourself.

_____

_____

_____

_____

I wish to forgive myself for the part I took in creating this
grievance. Specifically, I wish to forgive myself for:

_____

_____

_____

_____

_____

_____

_____

_____

_____

_____

_____

STEP FOUR: GAIN PERSPECTIVE

Exercise: Newspaper reporter

Pretend you are a newspaper reporter and write a short article about your forgiveness opportunity. Use the third person, and include only the facts (who, what, where, when, how).

_____

_____

_____

_____

_____

_____

_____

_____

_____

_____

_____

_____

_____

_____

Exercise: The wide-angle lens

What were the positive aspects or results of the situation? Did you learn something, develop skills; what gifts did you receive because of this? If sufficient time has not passed for this to become evident, imagine what benefits might come from this situation.

_____

_____

_____

_____

_____

_____

Exercise: The deathbed exercise

What will you remember of this at the end of your life? Will you even remember it? How?

_____

_____

_____

_____

_____

Exercise: The heavenly perspective

Sit quietly in your chair and either close your eyes or soft-focus them on a spot on the floor. Relax your body and take a deep breath.

Imagine yourself in your grievance story, with all of its problems, dark emotions, and difficulties. Picture a scene that represents the issues you are grappling with and picture yourself in the scene. What are you doing, feeling, and saying?

Once you get a clear picture of this scene, make a clone of your spirit and assign it the job of "observer." Make your observer spirit fly up to the rooftop to view this scene with your spirit's X-ray vision. What do you observe from the rooftop?

_____

_____

_____

_____

Now send your spirit up to the clouds and have it view the scene with you in it. What does your spirit observe from the clouds?

_____

_____

_____

_____

Now send your spirit up to the moon and have it view the scene with you in it. What does your spirit observe from the moon?

_____

_____

_____

_____

Now send your spirit up to heaven, where it can perceive all of the cosmos. Ask your spirit to view the scene back on earth. Then tell your spirit to consult with a Divine entity (you might call it God, Goddess, Allah, or others) to determine if there is a Divine meaning to what is going on in the scene on earth. Listen closely and note what your spirit tells you from heaven.

_____

_____

_____

_____

Come back to earth and slowly open your eyes. Breathe deeply.

Exercise: The hero perspective

In order to turn around a grievance story, you need to paint yourself as the hero in the story. Focus on the amazing resilience you showed—after all, you survived, didn't you? How were you the hero in this story?

_____

_____

_____

_____

_____

_____

_____

_____

_____

_____

_____

_____

_____

_____

_____

_____

_____

_____

_____

STEP FIVE: LETTING GO

Exercise: Entertaining the possibility of letting go

Are there any good reasons to hold on to your grievance story and all its negative emotions? Is there some benefit you would lose if you were to let go of your negative emotions about this?

_____

_____

_____

_____

_____

It is important to define a benefit for the process of forgiveness. When you get stuck in righteous feelings of being a victim, it is hard to imagine letting them go. However, a lot of mental and emotional energy goes into keeping your grievance story alive. Let's consider the benefits of not having the negative feelings and thoughts.

How would it feel if you could let go of your residual feelings and thoughts about the situation? How would you benefit from releasing your feelings about it?

_____

_____

_____

_____

_____

_____

_____

Exercise: Releasing emotions

Review the visual, auditory and kinesthetic letting go exercises found on pages 60-61.

Describe the exercise you did and how you feel now:

_____

_____

_____

_____

_____

_____

Exercise: Forgiveness meditation or prayer

May I be at peace.

May my heart remain open.

May I awaken to my inner Divine essence.

May I be healed.

May I be a source of healing for all beings.

May You be at peace.

May Your heart remain open.

May You awaken to your inner Divine essence.

May You be healed.

May You be a source of healing for all beings.

May We be at peace.

May our hearts remain open.

May We awaken to our inner Divine essence.

May We be healed.

May We be a source of healing for all beings.

Exercise: Write a forgiveness letter

Write a forgiveness letter to the person who hurt you, acknowledging the emotions that person might have felt, what their needs might have been, and what elements of their background might explain their actions.

_____

_____

_____

_____

_____

_____

_____

_____

_____

_____

Forgiveness
Opportunity
Six

_____

_____

_____

_____

_____

_____

_____

_____

_____

_____

Exercise: Write a forgiveness letter to yourself

Write yourself a forgiveness letter. Acknowledge your
feelings, your needs and what elements of your background
explain your actions or lack thereof. Write of your pride in the
good work you've done in this journal, and forgive yourself
for whatever you feel guilty or regretful about in the grievance
story. Know that heaven joins you in forgiving yourself, and
that you bask in the Divine's unending forgiveness, love and
acceptance of you, just as you are. You can write here in your
journal, or you can compose it on stationery, in which case you
will self-address the envelope, stamp it and mail it.

STEP SIX: TAKE ACTION

Plan your next action and notate it here:

_____

_____

_____

_____

_____

_____

STEP SEVEN: BLESS THE OTHER

What is the blessing you will repeat when you happen to think of your grievance story?

a
forgiveness
journal

_____

_____

_____

_____

_____

_____

CHAPTER FIFTEEN
Forgiveness Opportunity Seven

STEP ONE: IDENTIFY YOUR FEELINGS

Briefly describe the grievance story you wish to work on here:

_____

_____

_____

_____

_____

_____

Exercise: Identify your feelings

When you think of your forgiveness opportunity, what are the primary emotions that you feel? Please refer to the list on page 33.

_____

_____

_____

_____

_____

What were your unmet needs in the situation? Please refer to the list of human needs on page 35.

_____

_____

_____

_____

_____

Now, please write for about ten minutes about your deepest thoughts and emotions about your forgiveness opportunity. If you begin to feel a strong emotion, stay with it but try to observe it from an objective point of view. As you observe it in this manner, its intensity will fade.

The objective in this exercise is to notate your feelings and thoughts expressively as possible. Do not hold back on your emotions.

_____

_____

_____

_____

_____

STEP TWO: TALK IT OUT

Exercise: Talking it out

At some point, you may wish to share your forgiveness opportunity story with a friend, partner, or confidante.

Describe how your talk went and how you felt after it:

_____

_____

_____

_____

_____

_____

STEP THREE: CHANGE VIEWPOINTS

Exercise: Change viewpoints

Think about your grievance story and what you knew about the other person. What might have been going on in his life that made him act the way he did? For example, if your grievance story involves a parent, write about what aspects of her upbringing or the difficulties she was grappling with at the time of your story.

Or you can ask yourself, what would cause me to act this way? What could have happened to me to motivate me to do the same? What in my history, my beliefs, the way my parents raised me, the traumas, etc. might have caused me to be like the other person?

_____

_____

_____

_____

_____

Were there some challenges or difficulties she was facing? What else might he have been dealing with that you weren't aware of? What emotions might the other person have felt? Please refer to the list of emotions on page 33. What were the other person's needs? Please refer to the list of human needs on page 35. Take time to write about what the other person might have been feeling and what his needs were:

_____

_____

_____

_____

_____

_____

Exercise: Taking responsibility for your part

What did you do to contribute to the situation? In every situation, there is something—some action that you took or didn't take—that you feel responsible for. This is an account-ability step, and it also identifies what you may need to forgive in yourself.

_____

_____

_____

_____

_____

I wish to forgive myself for the part I took in creating this grievance. Specifically, I wish to forgive myself for:

_____

_____

_____

_____

STEP FOUR: GAIN PERSPECTIVE

Exercise: Newspaper reporter

Pretend you are a newspaper reporter and write a short article about your forgiveness opportunity. Use the third person, and include only the facts (who, what, where, when, how).

Exercise: The wide-angle lens

What were the positive aspects or results of the situation?
Did you learn something, develop skills; what gifts did you
receive because of this? If sufficient time has not passed for
this to become evident, imagine what benefits might come
from this situation.

_____

_____

_____

_____

_____

_____

Exercise: The deathbed exercise

What will you remember of this at the end of your life?
Will you even remember it? How?

_____

_____

_____

_____

_____

Exercise: The heavenly perspective

Sit quietly in your chair and either close your eyes or
soft-focus them on a spot on the floor. Relax your body and
take a deep breath.

Imagine yourself in your grievance story, with all of its
problems, dark emotions, and difficulties. Picture a scene
that represents the issues you are grappling with and picture
yourself in the scene. What are you doing, feeling, and saying?

Once you get a clear picture of this scene, make a clone of your spirit and assign it the job of "observer." Make your observer spirit fly up to the rooftop to view this scene with your spirit's X-ray vision. What do you observe from the rooftop?

_____

_____

_____

_____

Now send your spirit up to the clouds and have it view the scene with you in it. What does your spirit observe from the clouds?

_____

_____

_____

_____

Now send your spirit up to the moon and have it view the scene with you in it. What does your spirit observe from the moon?

_____

_____

_____

_____

Now send your spirit up to heaven, where it can perceive all of the cosmos. Ask your spirit to view the scene back on earth. Then tell your spirit to consult with a Divine entity (you might call it God, Goddess, Allah, or others) to determine if there is a Divine meaning to what is going on in the scene on earth. Listen closely and note what your spirit tells you from heaven.

_____

_____

_____

_____

Come back to earth and slowly open your eyes. Breathe deeply.

Exercise: The hero perspective

In order to turn around a grievance story, you need to paint yourself as the hero in the story. Focus on the amazing resilience you showed—after all, you survived, didn't you? How were you the hero in this story?

_____

_____

_____

_____

_____

_____

_____

_____

_____

_____

_____

_____

_____

_____

_____

_____

_____

_____

_____

STEP FIVE: LETTING GO

Exercise: Entertaining the possibility of letting go

Are there any good reasons to hold on to your grievance story and all its negative emotions? Is there some benefit you would lose if you were to let go of your negative emotions about this?

_____

_____

_____

_____

_____

_____

It is important to define a benefit for the process of forgiveness. When you get stuck in righteous feelings of being a victim, it is hard to imagine letting them go. However, a lot of mental and emotional energy goes into keeping your grievance story alive. Let's consider the benefits of not having the negative feelings and thoughts.

How would it feel if you could let go of your residual feelings and thoughts about the situation? How would you benefit from releasing your feelings about it?

_____

_____

_____

_____

_____

_____

_____

_____

Exercise: Releasing emotions

Review the visual, auditory and kinesthetic letting go exercises found on pages 60-61.

Describe the exercise you did and how you feel now:

_____

_____

_____

_____

_____

_____

Exercise: Forgiveness meditation or prayer

May I be at peace.

May my heart remain open.

May I awaken to my inner Divine essence.

May I be healed.

May I be a source of healing for all beings.

May You be at peace.

May Your heart remain open.

May You awaken to your inner Divine essence.

May You be healed.

May You be a source of healing for all beings.

May We be at peace.

May our hearts remain open.

May We awaken to our inner Divine essence.

May We be healed.

May We be a source of healing for all beings.

Exercise: Write a forgiveness letter

Write a forgiveness letter to the person who hurt you, acknowledging the emotions that person might have felt, what their needs might have been, and what elements of their background might explain their actions.

Forgiveness
Opportunity
Seven

Exercise: Write a forgiveness letter to yourself

Write yourself a forgiveness letter. Acknowledge your feelings, your needs and what elements of your background explain your actions or lack thereof. Write of your pride in the good work you've done in this journal, and forgive yourself for whatever you feel guilty or regretful about in the grievance story. Know that heaven joins you in forgiving yourself, and that you bask in the Divine's unending forgiveness, love and acceptance of you, just as you are. You can write here in your journal, or you can compose it on stationery, in which case you will self-address the envelope, stamp it and mail it.

STEP SIX: TAKE ACTION

Plan your next action and notate it here:

_____

_____

_____

_____

_____

_____

STEP SEVEN: BLESS THE OTHER

What is the blessing you will repeat when you happen to think of your grievance story?

_____

_____

_____

_____

_____

_____

CONCLUSION

CONGRATULATIONS FOR COMPLETING THIS FORGIVENESS Journal! I am proud of your good work, and I know that you are now traveling with a lighter energetic load.

You will find that the forgiveness process is never-ending. There may be times when you need to revisit some of the exercises in this Journal to dig a little deeper and release another layer of negativity. This is normal. Be gentle to yourself when this happens, and know that your continued efforts are evolving your soul to ever-higher realms.

You will also find that forgiving in the future is easier now that you've done the heavy lifting on your past. You have developed a spiritual muscle that remembers how and what to do when you encounter a forgiveness opportunity. You will be able to invoke some of the approaches and attitudes you discovered in working through this journal, and that you are able to forgive more quickly and with a little more ease than before.

I can assure you that your efforts to forgive are making our world a better place. As Gandhi said, "Be the change you wish to see." The changes that you effect on the inside of YOU make a profound difference in your world and the world at large. The change I wish to see is a more forgiving world, with people journeying through life with less resentment and more internal peace. Internal peace is always the precursor to external peace, so bravo for taking the first step toward peace on earth.

Thank you for making the world a better place! Blessings to you on your journey!

IF YOU'D LIKE MORE ON FORGIVENESS AND SPIRITUALITY...

Please visit our website at www.brioleadership.com, where you can stay connected with Kristin's latest thoughts and the community that follows her. Here are some of fun things you'll find there:

- A FREE offer in return for signing up to receive Kristin's monthly e-newsletter

- A FREE blog that publishes Kristin's musings on spiritual intelligence in the workplace and in daily life

- A link to Kristin's FREE personal spiritual blog

- Lots of FREE articles about living a full life, spirituality in everyday life, and bringing spiritual intelligence into the workplace

- Other product offerings such as spiritual jewelry and wearable art, information products such as on-line learning modules, and meditation CDs

You might also consider working directly with Kristin, either one-on-one or in a group setting. She offers the following services to corporations, non-profit groups and individuals:

One-on-One Coaching

Having a coach is like having a secret business or spiritual partner whose only concern is your success. Kristin can help you balance your life, incorporate your spirit into your work and family life, and help you achieve results that you never thought possible. She is certified to administer and coach to Conscious Pursuit's Spiritual Intelligence assessment instrument, which helps people identify their spiritual strengths and growth opportunities. She also uses a coaching program called Mindset for Success that is based on spiritual principles and enables people to break through limiting beliefs and achieve extraordinary results.

A Forgiveness Workshop

This workshop is an experiential seminar in which a group works through many of the exercises found in this book, plus many more than can only be done in person. The seminar can be done in a 4-hour condensed seminar, but for maximum benefit you might consider the 8-hour seminar. Corporations and non-profits will benefit from sponsoring this seminar, as forgiveness in workgroups is often lacking and sorely needed for better teamwork and higher productivity. You can bring Kristin onsite to conduct this seminar.

The Temple of Well-Being Workshop

This workshop addresses your innate need to reduce stress, balance our energies, and construct lives of meaning by helping you understand a human being's multiple intelligences, including spiritual intelligence. For organizations, it is important to build work environments that support each worker's multiple intelligences to create an engaged and productive workplace. This seminar is offered as a 4-hour introduction or an 8-hour experiential session that Kristin offers to corporations, non-profits, churches, and industry groups.

Please visit Brio Leadership at www.Brioleadership.com/contact to inquire about these exciting services.

ABOUT THE AUTHOR

KRISTIN ROBERTSON IS THE PRESIDENT and Head Coach of Brio Leadership. Her passion is to help individuals and teams positively transform their lives, using the principles of spiritual intelligence. Kristin is a spiritual intelligence coach, dynamic teacher, presenter, and consultant. For ten years, she was president of KR Consulting, a training and consulting firm that provides services to the technical support industry. She founded Brio Leadership to help leaders make a positive difference in their work environments. Before becoming an entrepreneur, Kristin worked as an executive in high technology and financial services companies.

Educated as a classical musician, Kristin received degrees in music performance. Currently, her only musical outlets are attending concerts and occasionally substituting as the keyboard player for her church's services. She brings both the creativity and the discipline of music to her spiritual practices.

Kristin's spiritual practices are eclectic. Raised in mainline Protestant churches, she has explored other faith traditions since college, including Judaism, feminine theology, and Buddhism. Currently a Unitarian Universalist, she is also exploring her Christian heritage by studying to be a Spiritual Director. She prays, meditates, chants, writes in a journal, and is always looking for new ways to connect with the Divine in everyday life.

Kristin lives in North Texas with her husband and two college-age children.

● ● ●

CPSIA information can be obtained at www.ICGtesting.com
Printed in the USA
BVOW02s0429170414

350822BV00003B/92/P

9 780982 341407